THE ABC'S OF FO'C'SLE LIVING

The ABC's
of Fo'c'sle Living

A.K. LARSSEN

and

SIG JAEGER

MADRONA PUBLISHERS, INC.

SEATTLE

Library of Congress Cataloging in Publication Data

Larssen, A K
  The ABC's of fo'c'sle living.

  "Part of this book appeared . . . in the Marine fisheries review vol. 36, no.
6, June 1974 under the title Some ABC's of fo'c'sle living."
  1. Fisheries. 2. Fisheries — Vocational guidance. I. Jaeger, Sig, joint
author. II. Title.
SH331.L37   639'.2'023   76-17265
ISBN 0-914842-11-0 (U.S.A.)
ISBN 0-88894-104-8 (Canada)

USA   CANADA
Madrona Publishers, Inc.   J.J. Douglas Ltd.
113 Madrona Place East   1875 Welch Street
Seattle, Washington 98112   North Vancouver, B.C.

Drawings by Ann Downs

Preface

CONCEIVED and written as a guide, or textbook, for use in extension courses and vocational classes for would-be commercial fishermen, the first — and major — part of this book appeared as a rather long article in the Marine Fisheries Review, Vol. 36, No. 6, June 1974 under the title "Some ABC's of Fo'c'sle Living."

Today the age-old trade of commercial fishing is not only a trade, but, rather, a complex mixture of the skills of a tradesman, the hard physical labor of a laborer, the seamanship of a knowledgeable seaman plus the business acumen of a successful business proprietor. Clearly, a young man entering the trade of commercial fishing will have much to learn. It seems appropriate to give budding fishermen a chance to profit by experience of those who have grown old in the trade, and that is why this little collection of do's and don'ts, of hints and suggestions, has been written.

Through the last part of the book you will find bits and pieces of the early history of commercial fishing in Pacific Northwest waters, and names of some of the men and events that started it; also, a brief description of some of the fishing gear most commonly used.

Thanks are due to Marine Fisheries Review for permission to reprint "Some ABC's For Fo'c'sle Living." Also, our thanks to Mr. Berhard Scudd, Director, International Halibut Commission, and to Mr. Alonzo T. Pruter, Deputy Director, Northwest Fisheries Center, and Mr. Jerry Jurkovich, Fisheries Biologist, Northwest Fisheries Center, Seattle, Washington for helpful suggestions and advice.

Contents

1. *Want to Be a Fisherman?* 3

2. *Living in the Fo'c'sle* 9

3. *Your Outfiit* 21

4. *On Duty in the Pilothouse* 27

5. *Working on Deck* 34

6. *The Tools of the Trade* 38

7. *About Marlinspike Seamanship* 50

8. *Responsibilities* 54

9. *The Hold* 58

10. *Your Medical Rights and Personal Care* 60

11. *Bits and Pieces* 66

12. *How Do You Get Paid?* 71

13. *Shore Leave* 75

14. *Take Care of the Catch!* 79

15. *Who Started All This?* 84

    Epilogue 97

    Glossary of Terms 101

THE ABC'S OF FO'C'SLE LIVING

CHAPTER 1

Want to Be a Fisherman?

So YOU want to be a commercial fisherman. Or you think you do. Before you make up your mind, it might be well to do a bit of checking to see how much you know about the life you are thinking of making your own.

Commercial fishing is a very old trade. No one knows just how old, but we do know that a fellow named Simon, known locally as "The Big Fisherman," and later in life and in other parts of the world as Saint Peter, the "Rock," operated fishing boats and nets on the Sea of Galilee some two thousand years ago.

Yes, commercial fishing has been going on for a long time. Still, you may not be too sure of what the terms *commercial fishing* and *commercial fisherman* really mean in everyday language.

Stated as briefly as possible, a commercial fisherman is a man who goes to sea and catches fish that he sells to a wholesale fish buyer, who in turn sells it to a retail fish dealer, who in his turn sells it to the person who wants to eat it.

Chances are that you have heard or read stories about the "wild and free and wonderful" life at sea. Maybe you have heard or read stories from bygone days about the romance of deep-water fishing, of wresting a living from the sea, and other stories in the same key. Or perhaps you smelled "romance" in the story about the dory fighting its way through

choppy seas in a blinding snowstorm, its crew of two strain-
ing their eyes to the utmost through the whirling snow for a
glimpse of their schooner and safety. Romance? The men
who pulled the heavy oaken oar while craning their necks
and staring into the snowstorm would have another name
for it.

Romance is many things to many people. You would do
well to forget the romance bit the moment you start packing
your sea bag for your first trip to the fishing grounds.

Perhaps you have heard or read tall stories about the
money being made in commercial fisheries. Rest assured
that such stories are true — mostly. Big money has been
earned, is being earned, and will continue to be earned by
commercial fishermen.

The trouble is that this big money isn't being passed along
to all the participants. Some fishermen do earn big incomes,
but others earn barely enough for a skimpy living. A goodly
number — the unlucky ones, the unfit ones, or the victims of
short fishing seasons — earn only a part of a living and must
seek the rest elsewhere or accept such public help as unemployment compensation.

The fisherman's income is pretty much like the sea upon
which it is earned: it ebbs and it floods; just like the tide, but
not with tidal regularity, mind you!

We know of one fellow who earned just a few coins short of
eleven hundred bucks inside a twenty-hour workday. This
same man, on another occasion, spent three weeks —
twenty-one solid days — fighting strong winds and currents,
snowstorms, ice-covered decks, snarls on the gear, and all
the rest, and as payment for all his labors and miseries
received a paycheck for three cents: three small pieces of
copper for three weeks' hard work. So you see, it floods, but it
also ebbs.

Commercial fishing is a rather complex business, and the
status of a commercial fisherman is equally complex. He is a
workingman who performs back-breakingly hard work for
unnaturally long work hours. But he is also a man who has
pooled his time, strength, skill, and a certain amount of

money with a number of his fellows, fitted out a vessel, and gone to sea in search of fish that he hopes to sell at a profit. The cost of outfitting a fishing vessel for deep-water fishing is high, and each fisherman is responsible for his share of that cost. Thus he is risking not only his time and his work, but also a certain amount of cold cash each time he goes to sea in quest of fish, which makes him a businessman as well as a workingman.

The fisherman is on nobody's payroll and will not be handed a paycheck or pay envelope each Friday at quitting time; his earnings are derived directly and proportionately from his catch of fish and the price he obtains for same. The settlement at the end of the trip may bring him a large check or a small one. Or none at all. He may, indeed, get a bill for his share of the outfit instead of a check. That is called "going in the hole," "or getting a hole bill." This does not happen very often — but it does happen.

A fisherman's workday is a long one by anybody's standards. An eight-hour day for the commercial fisherman cannot even be a dream, because it is an impossibility. He can generally figure on being on deck sixteen to eighteen hours before he can remove oilskins and boots, but there will be occasions when his watch on deck may be twice as much, or more. If the deep-water fisherman manages to get three or four hours' sleep out of each twenty-four, he is doing well enough, all things considered.

A fisherman's home for the better part of each year is a small, crowded fo'c'sle shared with several other men. He knows but little of the home life shore-bound men know and love. More than one fisherman has been so much and so long away from home that his youngest offspring forgot what he looked like, and only uncertainly accepted him as a member of the family when he finally returned to home port.

There you have a rough sketch of what the life of a commercial fisherman is like: hard and dangerous work; long working hours; uncertain and highly variable income; spartan, crowded living quarters; long absences from home.

Still, the deep-water fisherman goes fishing. Why?

Perhaps Johan Bojer, in his book *The Last of the Vikings*, gave the answer: "in the winter [they] sailed hundreds of miles in open boats up to Lofoten, perhaps tempted by hope of gain, but too because on the sea they were free men."

There you have one possible answer: *free men*. Independent men. And the fisherman usually is a fiercely independent cuss, who takes great pride in his independence. He receives no wages, so he has no boss in the usual sense of the word. He has a skipper, sure, but the skipper is his leader, his commanding officer, but not his boss in the way a factory owner or manager is a boss. The skipper is himself a fisherman, the top fisherman on board and leader of his gang, or crew: it is his knowledge and skill and judgment that, in large measure, determine whether or not a payload of fish comes on board, which in turn means the success or failure of the fishing trip or fishing season. So the skipper runs the vessel and the crew toward that end, to the very best of his ability. He is the boss in the sense of being the leader. He knows what should be done, and when, and gives orders to that effect; and his orders must be obeyed without question. A competent fisherman might (silently) disagree with the skipper's decision, but he would never dream of refusing to obey the order.

A skipper may fire a fisherman for good and sufficient reason. The fisherman, on the other hand, may pack his sea bag and step ashore at the end of a trip for any reason he can think of, or for no reason at all that he would care to voice.

Do you see why the deep-water fisherman cherishes his status as an independent fellow, and why men become deep-water fishermen? If you stay with the fishing industry, you will find your own reasons (or rationalizations) for remaining with it. Later on in this book we attempt to describe some values other fishermen have found in their lives at sea.

All right. If you still believe you would like to become a commercial fisherman, read on about some of the customs fishermen follow, their lifestyle, and their values.

Some of the things we say are repeated and rephrased, for reasons you will come to understand. After a season or two of

BRISTOL BAY SAILBOAT

fishing, rereading this should be a bore, because you will have absorbed it all. But the tips included here, if they ease you into "the club" with a little less friction and with fewer personal problems, will have served their purpose.

CHAPTER 2

Living in the Fo'c'sle

You have made up your mind to become a commercial fisherman, that is, to make your living on the water. Fine! A good commercial fisherman is a most useful critter — and your intention, naturally, is to be a *good* fisherman.

Your life as a commercial fisherman will not only have you working on a fishing vessel; it will also mean that you will be living on that vessel for the better part of the year. Full-time deep-water fishermen (the ones who make commercial fishing pay them a rather high income) may spend up to 250 — or more — days of the year at sea. And, in addition, they spend a good many days on the dock or on the deck mending and building the fishing gear used at sea.

On board the fishing vessel, the *fo'c'sle* will be your home, your living room, bedroom, basement, and in many cases, your kitchen and dining room as well. By the way, fo'c'sle is old sailor-slang for forecastle, that low, dark, wet hole beneath the forecastle head (fo'c'sle head) which served as the sailor's home away from home on board the old sailing ships.

The fo'c'sle on board the fishing vessel is a good many notches above that on board the old windjammers. Your fo'c'sle will be warm, dry, and well lighted, as clean and cozy as you want it to be.

Most fishing boats today have living quarters in an upper deckhouse. The sleeping quarters are generally separate from the galley. The very modern, new king-crab-type vessels have two-bunk staterooms with such amenities as an intercom, desk, and sink in each. There is an increasing range in the variety and quality of crew quarters because there is such a range of boats: larger vessels, both old and new, as well as smaller ones.

Living in a fo'c'sle on a fishing boat is in several ways quite different from living in a house or an apartment ashore. Clearly, if you intend to go into that kind of life you must learn its do's and don'ts; you must learn to adapt to the fisherman's particular kind of living.

There are, in fact, quite a few procedures you must learn. Some of the customs mentioned here may seem small or petty to you now. Right you are! They are small and petty, taken one by one. In the aggregate, however, they amount to this: guidelines which, if followed, will make you into a dependable and pleasant shipmate, esteemed and respected by your fellows. Your life in the fo'c'sle will be a pleasant and rewarding experience. To not follow these customs will make you an undesirable shipmate, one who is somewhat less than beloved both in the fo'c'sle and on deck. Your own happiness on board will be . . . well, you can figure that one out for yourself. Thus it is in the best interests of everyone that budding fishermen learn the rules and live by them.

The very first thing you must learn is to keep yourself inside the railings of your vessel. Safety first, always. While under way, don't try to use the railing for an easy chair or a sofa. Do not sit, lie down, or walk on the railing!

Need a bucketful of clean sea water? Don't wrap the draw-bucket lanyard around your hand! And, don't drop the bucket overboard before your other hand has secured a good grip in a shroud, a guy line, or some other dependable anchor. In short, stay inside the railings. If the ugly scream of "man overboard" is ever heard on board your vessel, let it not be *you* they are screaming about.

Don't climb shrouds, stays, or guy lines. Keep out of the rigging entirely, unless ordered by the skipper to go up there for a valid reason: to replace a burnt-out light bulb, for instance.

USING THE DRAW BUCKET

In the fo'c'sle, your bunk and locker are your only private territory; the rest of the fo'c'sle must be shared equally with your shipmates. Equally means just that: all inhabitants are equal, and no one may use, or demand to use, more space than the next one. That also means you may not throw your clothes and other personal belongings wherever you like. Somewhere in the neighborhood of your bunk you will have a clothes hook, perhaps even two, that are your very own, and that is where your clothes must be placed when you undress for the bunk or change into your going-ashore clothes.

Keep in mind that the clothes hanging from a hook, whether on the bulkhead or in a clothes locker, must be secured so they do not swing as the boat rolls, which it does almost constantly. More than one coat or shirt has been worn threadbare early in its life from rubbing against the bulkhead.

Your clean spare clothes belong in your locker, as do your toilet articles, reading and writing matter, cigarettes, gum, candy, and whatever else in the way of small personal stuff you may pack along with you. This should include identification, especially a naturalization or birth certificate as proof of citizenship. This proof is necessary if you re-enter the country from a foreign port, which does sometimes happen during the trip. Birth certificates can be photocopied in a handy wallet size and plasticized for a dollar or two, and the original kept home in a safe place. For naturalization certificates, which may not be photocopied, get a citizenship identification card from the immigration station nearest you.

A man's fo'c'sle locker is his most private territory on board. Do not ever go into a shipmate's locker to borrow a pack of cigarettes or a pair of gloves or anything at all without first getting his permission to do so.

Keep your fo'c'sle clean! In a good crew, everyone takes his turn at washing the floor, the benches, the table, and the companionway; wiping out the wash basin; sprucing up the stove; and putting things in good order. On the run, or while weatherbound in harbor, bring your bedding on deck and give it a good airing, weather permitting.

The ship's toilet (often called the *head*) is, in a manner of speaking, a part of your living quarters and must be treated as such. Keep your toilet clean.

Be aware that the method of flushing the toilet on board a fishing vessel may be quite different from the one you are used to ashore. On some boats there is an electrically driven pump furnishing the water needed for flushing, but on many fishing boats, especially the older ones, the flushing water is nothing more than a part of the engine's cooling water piped through the toilet bowl, which means that there is no flushing water except when the main engine is running. There is a draw bucket, though, for use whenever the main engine is not running. Be sure to use that bucket! And to save someone else embarrassment, delay, and a frayed temper, if you use the last of that roll of necessary paper, *you* replace it.

Keep yourself and your clothing as clean as work and

conditions will allow. Fish can be pretty smelly critters; that's all right, for a fish. But there is no good reason why a fisherman should smell like a fish. Many of the modern fishing vessels, especially those engaged in the king-crab fishery, have automatic washing machines and clothes dryers on board. With such labor savers close at hand, and for free, a fisherman has no excuse for going around in dirty clothes, smelling like a spoiled fish. To keep your carcass clean at sea is also becoming less and less of a problem as more and more fishing vessels install shower stalls on board. Even so, use no more water than necessary.

Because of the long irregular hours and the hurry to get to bed, many fishermen tend to forget the regular habits of cleanliness. Most noticeable among such personal matters is neglect of the teeth. An old jam jar is a good container in which to keep brush and toothpaste and to take, full of water, out on deck for at least one daily brushing. And a washcloth does a good scrub job, better than the hands-only process.

Especially on board the older and the smaller fishing boats, the fresh-water tank is all too often pitifully small and the supply of fresh water inadquate by shore-side standards. Nothing much can be done about that except to learn to live with it: that is, to learn to use fresh water with great care.

On such a boat, a green man does well to watch what the rest of the crew does regarding water. Ask the cook. He is usually the one that will get the bawling-out from the skipper if the fresh-water tank runs dry before the trip is finished. Remember, there is an abundance of clean sea water close enough at hand, though it is not just as good. Still and all, fish blood, slime, and gurry can be removed quite effectively by washing in clean sea water. So there is no need to go into the galley, the fo'c'sle, or your bunk without first having removed some 99 percent of the blood, slime, and gurry from your hands, arms, and face. When you are on a long trip and far from home, and have several days' running time ahead of you, take a sea-water sponge bath before you put on a clean union suit; your homeward run will be more pleasant for yourself and for your shipmates as well.

On some fishing vessels, especially the halibut schooners and some of the older seine-boat types, the galley is located in the fo'c'sle. In such a fo'c'sle, where your bunk will be only a few feet removed from the stove, extra tact (not to mention neatness and cleanliness) is of the utmost importance. For instance, if you are in your bunk, get out of there the moment the cook begins to set the table. If you don't move out of your bunk before the rest of the fellows are seated at table, stay where you are until they have finished eating. Not one of them will want the dust of your blankets as seasoning for his food, you can be sure!

The cook on a fishing vessel, especially on a smaller one where the cook must help with some of the work on deck, is not "living the life of Riley"; he has a man-sized job on his hands and deserves your being as considerate and helpful as your own work permits. Here are a few examples of what you can do by way of helping: carry the slop bucket on deck for emptying, washing, and scrubbing; take rubber mats or other fo'c'sle floor coverings on deck to scrub and hang up to dry; help wash the dishes; dress and trim the fish the cook wants to serve for dinner. Otherwise, stay out of the way when he is cooking.

The *mug-up* is a between-meal occasion when massive sandwiches are sometimes made from the variety of meats, sausages, and other goodies that are always available in good quantity and quality on most fishing boats. But this can also be the source of problems for a greenhorn (or *in-breaker*) the first time he goes on a trip.

If you help yourself to a cup of coffee and a slice of bread for mug-up, be sure to wash and put away your cup and your knife or whatever tools you may have used. And that also means replacing the lid on the jam jar and putting it back in place, unless you find satisfaction in getting chewed out by a savage cook because the jar rolls off the table and spills when the boat heaves.

It is uncanny how quickly a man learns not to leave a cup

or jar unattended on the table when he cleans up the mess himself. But it is not an easy habit to acquire when your life to date has been spent ashore where the coffee cup stays in place no matter where you set it down.

Even seasoned fishermen, after some months ashore, when suddenly restricted to a small boat with several days of running time to the fishing grounds, get constipated. This can be painful, and can even be a source of seasickness.

The best preventatives for constipation are: eat lightly, and don't neglect roughage like fruit and vegetables; and get out of that bunk or off the bench in the galley. If the weather is so rough that you can't pace the deck, do a few bending exercises to get things moving.

The bunk on a long run can be a sleep trap, especially if you are bored; but sometimes in bad weather, getting into your bunk is the only thing left to do besides standing a wheel watch. Even reading is difficult and seems to induce more sleep, even after a ten-hour nap.

Courtesy is a very inexpensive commodity, so be courteous! It costs not a penny to say "thank you" when the cook does some small service for you, or "would you please" when you ask him to perform such a service.

The source of hot water for that shave (if you don't have a battery-operated shaver) may not be a self-replenishing tank, but a large kettle on top of the stove. Use what you need, but replace the water you've used as a courtesy to the cook and your shipmates who will want hot water next.

On the run to and from the fishing grounds, or when anchored up in a harbor, most of the crew will be in the fo'c'sle most of the time. If the galley is also in the fo'c'sle, keep out of the cook's way while he is preparing your next meal. If you have a card game going, or if you are using the galley table as a writing desk, keep an eye on how the cook's work is progressing and clear your stuff away in good time before the cook is ready to set the table. In short, give the cook all the help you can, directly and indirectly, whether the galley is located in the fo'c'sle or on deck.

Many men have strong feelings on various subjects such as

religion, politics, marriage, and the like. A calm discussion of such subjects may be all right, but emotion-filled arguments should be avoided. If you are taking part in such a discussion and you notice that one of your shipmates begins to get emotionally stirred, break off the discussion at once! Take a trip out on deck, grab a magazine and start reading, crawl into your bunk, do whatever is necessary to stop that discussion from turning into an argument. Emotional arguments are bad business in a fo'c'sle!

Don't be a smart-alec or a know-it-all. No one knows it all. Don't be a "sea lawyer"; he is the fellow who can put things to rights, who claims, "I know the law, by golly!" in any and all situations. He may think he knows but he wouldn't do you much good in a courtroom.

Don't be a "pilothouse rat," a carrier of tales between pilothouse and the fo'c'sle or deck, or between the skipper and the crew. A tired and overworked man (whether in the pilothouse or on deck) may be exceedingly irritable. He may under certain circumstances utter words that may be somewhat less than complimentary to the skipper or to his vessel, words that he does not really mean, which he secretly regrets having spoken. Such words should not be carried to the pilothouse (or from the pilothouse to fo'c'sle or deck). The same goes for rumors or gossip. The men who do such rumor mongering and gossiping are called pilothouse rats, and they are abundantly deserving of that name. Let it be noted, in all fairness, that there are not very many such in the fishing fleets. Let it be noted further, that most skippers do not enjoy having such an animal on board and will not dream of shipping one.

Don't be a crybaby. There is no need to tell your partner or the rest of your shipmates how cruelly your back, your hands, or your arms are hurting you. Your shipmates, too, are equipped with such parts and are using them just as much as you are using yours.

One of us once worked with a fisherman who suffered an acute attack of arthritis in both hands right at the beginning of what was to be a long and dirty-weather halibut trip.

Every joint in his hands swelled up, completely out of shape. All during the nine days of fishing and for several days of the home run, he couldn't button the fly of his pants, nor could he use knife and fork at table; his fingers couldn't be bent enough to grasp such slender tools. His pain must have been excruciating, but he never did mention it — not one word. He never missed a watch on deck, and he performed his full share of the work with a pair of hands that looked like deformed bear claws. All without a word of complaint. That is a picture of a *tough* man. We admired him immensely and silently; to give voice to our admiration would have been too embarrassing for all parties.

Avoid gambling on board the fishing vessel. A friendly (or even a well-heated) card game just for the fun of winning can be a relaxing and pleasant pastime on a long run or on harbor days. When money comes into the game, however, the relaxed atmosphere will change, slowly but steadily, to an atmosphere of tension that grows in proportion to the money invested.

Many years ago in the days of the "smoke boats" (the halibut steamers), gambling on board ship was not only common, it was a plague and a curse. On the long runs from Seattle or Vancouver, B.C. to the Alaska fishing grounds and back, there was plenty of spare time, and a poker or blackjack or rummy game was in progress for days on end. Some men became so enamoured with the game that they didn't have time to take their turns at the wheel; they hired a non-gambling shipmate to perform that duty for them. The inevitable result was, of course, that many a fisherman gambled away his share of the trip even before the fish had been sold. Coming home from a month-long trip with a full load of fish — but minus a paycheck — such a fisherman would catch a bit of well-deserved hell from his wife and his creditors, which led him to develop some hard feelings against the shipmate, or mates, who had won his money away from him. The hard feelings sometimes developed into long-lasting enmity between men who otherwise would have been friends.

You have no doubt been taught manners — that is, certain accepted modes of behavior in your association with other members of *Homo sapiens*. Do not leave your manners behind when you go on board your fishing vessel: on the contrary, be sure to bring your manners along with you. In the cramped quarters of the fo'c'sle and galley, good manners are needed even more than they are needed ashore!

If there is a basket of toast or bread on the table, don't get into the habit of fingering several pieces before you take one, although it's acceptable and perceptive to take the second slice down in the stack: the top slice is usually dried out if the bread has been on the table for a while.

On some boats, each man has his fixed place at table. If your place happens to be on the bench up against the bulk-head behind the table, or if your seat happens to be in the middle of the bench with one man or more on each side of you, be sure to get yourself into your seat before the man on the outside of you sits down, or else he must get up and out to let you into your seat. A small, petty thing! You may think so, but you would change your thinking soon enough if you happened to be the man on the outside seat and always had to get up in order to let another fellow in.

On other boats you may sit wherever you like, except in the skipper's seat; the skipper has his fixed seat, which no one else may occupy. It may be at either end of the table, or in some other spot from which he can get up hurriedly and get out on deck if occasion demands it, without disturbing the rest of the table.

The importance of observing good manners, courtesy, and common decency on board the fishing vessel cannot be overemphasized. One of the important items in this category is habits of speech. Rough language is not exactly standard on board fishing vessels, but it cannot be said to be a novelty, either. Some men use such language simply because they lack sufficient vocabulary; others, especially youngsters, adopt rough language in an attempt to sound tough, like what they believe an old sea dog sounds like.

Rough, earthy words are part of our language, and they have their uses, certainly. But what habitual use of such language will do for you when ashore is stamp you as ill mannered, almost but not quite civilized. Your shipmates will not take offense, but these habits, as we all know, are easy to get into and hard to get out of.

While speaking of manners and of words, let's have a quick look at some words that may never be spoken on board a fishing vessel, and look at a few other superstitions. Not that all fishermen are superstitious, of course, but some of them are, and their superstitions are so old and so well ingrained, that to argue about them won't alter anything but tempers.

There are forbidden words that no one may utter, either on deck or in fo'c'sle: *horse*, *pig*, or *hog*. They are taboo. According to an old and well-established superstition, the mere mention of one of those animals is enough to bring bad weather, poor fishing, snarls on your gear, a line in the propeller, or any other trouble you care to mention. It is deemed to be very bad manners, if nothing worse, to mention these unmentionable words.

Don't turn the hatch cover upside down! Such carelessness will surely bring a southwest storm over your head. Don't bring a black suitcase on board a fishing boat; bad luck galore will be the result of such foolhardiness, as bad as if you were to break a mirror, although not quite as bad as bringing an umbrella on board. That's the very last straw, and anything is liable to happen to the fishing, the vessel, and to each and every man on board.

Don't harm the gony birds, or annoy them in any manner. If you do, you will soon feel the wrath of those who believe that each gony is the embodiment of a sailor or fisherman — often a former shipmate — lost at sea.

The men of the purse-seine fleet have a few rules all their own. Don't accept anything edged — such as a knife or scissors — as a gift; you must pay for it with a penny, or it will sever your friendship with the giver. On board a purse seiner, don't trim your fingernails while sitting on the seine pile, or you will cause the seine to hit a snag before the day is done, "mark my words, young feller!" While on the fishing grounds, don't lend anything at all to a man from another vessel: you'll be giving away your luck for the rest of the day, and maybe for the rest of the season. Do not hand a bar of soap to a shipmate while washing up at the end of a long workday. It's all right to drop the soap into his wash basin, though. If you have to open a can of fruit or whatever, be sure that the top end of the can is up before you put the can opener to work. Cutting the bottom out of a can is said to be very bad business.

Just superstitions? Indeed they are, but no greenhorn should attempt to play fast and loose with an old-timer's superstitions. That is bad manners with a captial B!

CHAPTER 3

Your Outfit

You are going to sea as a full-time fisherman, which means that you are going to sea to live as well as to work. Living on a boat is in several respects very different from living ashore; one of the things you need for successful living afloat is special clothing which may differ a great deal from your shoreside garb.

Chances are that you have never been health-conscious, that you have never seen any particular reason for taking care of your health. Such care is quite necessary at sea, however, because a commercial fisherman can't call his doctor or send a boy up to the drugstore. He can't just call the office and announce, "I won't be in today. Got a nasty cold. Going to stay in bed all day." No sir, the fisherman must go on deck and attend to the business of getting a trip of fish on board, cold or no cold. Therefore, he must do his best to prevent that cold from getting started. And this is why you need special clothing: to protect your health as best you can.

What kind of clothing should you wear at sea for your health and comfort? Let's begin with the underwear which should be all or mostly wool. Wool does not get cold when wet, and as a commercial fisherman you will certainly get your underwear wet from perspiration, if not from that breaker over the railing which is bound to give you a greeting sooner or later.

Among deep-sea fishermen, the wool union suit, a one-piece garment, is commonly in use, although a few men prefer the two-piece system. One piece or two? No matter, only let it be wool. Your fishing shirt and pants should also be of wool. Fishermen generally cut their shirt sleeves about halfway between the elbow and the end of the cuff. That cut should be served (cross-stitched) with woolen yarn to prevent unraveling.

A wristlet is a tube of knitted wool, sometimes wool and nylon, with a short narrow thumbstrap sewn onto one end, dividing the opening into two spaces, one larger, the other smaller. The wristlet, as indicated by its name, is made to protect your wrist and forearm: the smaller opening fits the base of your thumb; the larger one, the rest of your hand almost down to the knuckles. The body of the wristlet is pulled up over your forearm and part of your shirt sleeve to well above the elbow, where it is fastened by means of two strong, fairly large, safety pins. A set of wristlets — or wristers as they are commonly called — is an important item of clothing for a deep-sea fisherman. They help to keep your wrists warm, thus helping to prevent stiffness and soreness of the joints; they protect the skin of your forearms from being scratched or torn by the gear you are working, such as web, hooks, and lines; and they prevent the cuffs of your oilskin coat from chafing your wrists.

Rubber boots should be large enough to allow air to circulate around your feet; even a small amount of circulating air will minimize the natural rubber-boot dampness to some degree. Woolen socks are as a rule worn outside cotton socks; cotton socks are worn inside sheepskin bootlets. Whatever the combination, have it on when trying on new boots.

The boot may be of the three-quarter-length or of the full-length variety; it's a matter of personal preference. The three-quarter-length boot is heavily built, strong, and not easily punctured. It is easy to get into and can be kicked off with comparative ease in case of an emergency.

Some men prefer the full-length boots (hip boots), the type used by steelhead fishermen. These boots are light and easy to pack around with you. They are insulated from the ankle down and are warm enough so that woolen socks and bootlets are not needed; a thin inner sole and ordinary shore socks will suffice. Being light, these boots cannot take the punishment that can be meted out to the stiffer but more heavily built boots. All boots are susceptible to rips, tears, and punctures (by spines of dogfish, rockfish, etc.) and must be treated with a degree of care. Also, full-length boots must generally be suspended from the pants belt with a lanyard.

If these light sport-type boots are used, a pair of suspenders for the pants may be a good idea. Some fishermen prefer suspenders anyway, because they give greater freedom around the waist.

Boot types will vary considerably according to the type of work, sea conditions, and so forth. Inshore fishermen might use only knee-length boots. As a guide, note what is the most-used boot on your vessel.

In the offshore fishery, the heavy-duty, three-quarter-length boot seems most popular. It is stiff enough to remain extended without having to be suspended from a belt, and extends only halfway up between the knee and the hip. It is convenient to get on and off, which may also pay dividends in an emergency, like after falling overboard.

Oilskin pants outside the boots may bind the knees. By pulling up the oilskin pants several inches and putting a heavy-duty rubber band around the pants leg, you get needed freedom and may prevent your boots from filling up if an extra-large breaker comes aboard.

Oilskins — rain gear, shore people call them. Not so in the fishing fleets, where we still use the traditional name, oilskins, although modern oilskins have nothing at all to do with oil (the word originated when cotton cloth painted with a mixture of linseed oil and wax was used for wear in wet weather, replacing real animal skins).

There are any number of brands and qualities of oilskins available: all rubber, rubberized, vinyl coated and so forth. The vinyl-coated types are excellent, resistant as they are to oil, grease, acid, and chemicals. Oilskins come in several colors: yellow, black, gray, green, etc. Be sure that the oilskins *you* buy are of a bright yellow hue. That bright color might save your life one night if you should go overboard.

It is not a good idea to look for bargains when you go out to buy your first outfit of fishing clothes. Such bargains can turn out to be very costly indeed! The proper place to get your outfit is at a fishermen's outfitting store. Such stores carry all the stuff you need; their clerks are trained men, professionals who know your needs even better than you do yourself, and they are ready and willing to give you sound advice. Also, an outfitting store will let you have your outfit on credit if you should need it.

If the boat on which you have shipped trades at the store, your store bill will be deducted from your check at the time of settlement. If not, it will be to your advantage to pay your store bill promptly upon receiving your check. One of the worst things that can happen to a fisherman's name is to get a reputation for not paying his bills. Once you have earned that kind of reputation you'll soon find it difficult to get a job on board a decent vessel — and impossible to get credit. The word has a way of getting around.

What and how much to buy? Here is a list as a general guide, the bare minimum, mind you. Items will vary, depending on the fishery.

> 2 sets underwear
> 2 fishing shirts
> 2 pairs fishing pants
> 2 pairs wristlets
> 2 pairs socks
> 1 pair deck slippers
> 2 pairs bootlets (ankle-high absorbent oversocks)
> 2 pairs oil pants (you should have a spare pair on board!)
> 1 oil jacket
> 1 pair boots
> 1 sou'wester

A small sewing kit with needles, thread, wool yarn, and a few buttons is necessary equipment for the deep-sea fisherman, as is an inner-tube mending kit for repair of boots. If you are a habitual user of cigarettes, candy, or chewing gum, be sure that you take along an adequate supply of these items.

If you smoke cigarettes and the boat operates at sea outside the three-mile territorial limit, sea stores may be purchased by the skipper through the customhouse. Liquor is also available if the skipper so chooses, but few do. Sea stores are tax free, and these cigarettes and liquor cost about one-half of shore-side prices. These items must be kept locked up in port, cannot be taken ashore, and must be consumed at sea. Heavy fines and removal of the sea-stores privilege can be the consequence of violations. Ask your skipper about this. Many skippers buy the cigarettes but generally do not permit liquor aboard while at sea.

Gloves should be bought according to need, which depends upon what kind of fishery you are going into. The clerk in the outfitting store will give you good advice here. If you are entering the trawl fishery, where you must handle used or old wire rope, be sure to get a pair of good heavy leather gloves for wire-rope work.

On a longline vessel, you must furnish your own *hook set*, a rather simple tool used for bringing a bent fishhook back into its proper shape. Ask one of the gang to show you how to make one before leaving on your first trip. You'll also have to buy yourself a splicer, the small wooden-handled *marlinspike* used for "sticking gear" and for splicing halibut longlines. Yes, and you need to buy a good pocket knife, also!

One more item to buy: bedding. Some fishing vessels furnish a mattress for your bunk, but some of the older ones don't — you must pack your own. Many men prefer a good heavy air mattress, others prefer foam rubber.

Air mattresses may be inflated to whatever hardness is preferred. A rule of thumb is that when sitting on an air mattress, your bottom should just touch the bunk boards. Therefore, when you're lying down, the mattress will sup-

port all your body contours. An air mattress is very convenient to deflate, roll up, and put in your sea bag when
moving ashore or to another boat.

If you get an air mattress, be certain that you have a
patching kit. Punctures from chafing and nailheads in the
bunk cause air leaks, sometimes at awkward times. The
likelihood of air leaks increases with the age and the quality
of the mattress.

In a foam-rubber mattress, hardness is constant. It may be
rolled up for transport, but will fill the sea bag and then
some. Its useful life is virtually indefinite, so choose with
care, as it will be many years before you must buy another
one. The cost of a foam-rubber mattress may be higher than
for an air mattress, but this may depend on the quality of air
mattress you have in mind.

Foam-rubber pillows are preferred by many fishermen.
They do not ball up or form lumps. Hardness is constant.

Sheets are not generally used on board fishing boats.
Blankets, yes, if you prefer them. A sleeping bag with two or
more washable liners is by far the easiest and most practical
bedding.

Be aware that what is said here about proper fishing
clothes does not hold true for the summer fisherman, such as
the seine and/or gillnet fisherman operating on inside waters, such as in Puget Sound, or the Gulf of Georgia, or
southeast Alaska. For summer (inside) fishing almost any old
clothes will do. Oilskins, boots, and gloves, however, are
musts in any waters, any time of year. Note also that in the
purse-seine and gillnet fishery, a skirt or an apron is often
used instead of oil pants. And do not forget that a sou'wester
is part of a suit of oilskins.

CHAPTER 4

On Duty in the Pilothouse

ON BOARD the fishing vessel a part of your duty will be performed in the pilothouse: standing wheel watch. This is a small part of your work if reckoned in hours and minutes, but a very important part. When you go on wheel watch you are assuming a serious responsibility; your watchfulness and your reactions before a dangerous situation develops, may well determine life or death for yourself, your shipmates, and your vessel.

Your experience probably will have to be gained in many pilothouses, under many skippers. Each will have his own rules or method of operation; each will have personal traits you may or may not like. It will be well to remember that you and your shipmates also have your quirks and your foibles. But, in the tight little floating community of which you are now a member, everyone must learn to get along with everyone else. Each of your paychecks must come out of that load of fish you are trying to get on board. And first and foremost, you must learn to get along with your skipper.

Each time you enter the pilothouse these first months at sea, take half a second to remember that you are indeed a novice — a greenhorn, in fishermen's vernacular — with practically everything to learn in this new and strange occupation. You cannot learn all you need to know from this book or from any number of books. The knowledge you must acquire in order to become a competent and dependable all-round fisherman/seaman, fully trustworthy anywhere on board, including the pilothouse, must be learned in the only way possible — by experience. And that is just what you now are trying to do: gain experience. Still, it will do you no harm to know, even before you enter the pilothouse, some of the things you must or must not do when you make your debut and take your first "turn at the wheel."

The first thing you must learn is to obey orders, quickly and without back talk. You must do that on deck, too, of course; it is, however, still more important in the pilothouse. Bear in mind that perhaps one day *you* will be the one who gives orders. We have an old and very true axiom which tells us that "one must learn to *obey* orders before one can learn to *give* orders."

The skipper will specify where or when he wants to be called, and this order should be strictly observed. In addition, you must call the skipper if and when you are uncertain about any item relevant to the safety and well-being of the vessel such as a course change, on which side to take an on-coming vessel, cross traffic, sudden loss of visibility due to fog, rain-thick, or snowfall, sudden or violent increase in wind, or any situation in which you think you must make an unscheduled change in course or speed. In short — when in doubt as to the proper course of action, call the skipper. Remember, the very fact that you are in doubt means that you are not quite ready to make your own decision in the matter.

Your job in the pilothouse is not just to steer the boat; it is first and foremost to keep the skipper informed, to be his eyes and ears when he is away from the pilothouse, whether in his bunk or in the galley.

The skipper must be kept informed; once he knows the problem, he will do his own thinking, make his own decisions, and take the full responsibility for the consequences of those decisions.

A second and very important thing to learn right away is how to slow down the engine and disengage the clutch when the need arises. Your skipper or engineer (if there is one on board) will show you how; if they forget or neglect to do so, ask to be shown. Here is why: If and when you collide with a log or other fair-sized piece of driftwood, you must throttle down the engine and disengage the clutch in order to prevent the debris from getting caught by the propeller. There will be no time to think it over. Your action must come quickly — instantly — upon your hitting the object if you are to prevent damage to your propeller. You must know beforehand which movements to make so that one hand can reach for the throttle while your other hand goes to the clutch-control lever.

A log, or even a not-so-large piece of driftwood, can do a great deal of damage, such as bending a propeller blade or the propeller shaft. Either one is a costly affair, not only for the vessel's owner who pays the bills for dry-docking and repairs, but perhaps even more for the crew because valuable fishing days, maybe the whole trip, may be lost. Which brings us to a fact worth remembering: lost time, whether hours or days, cannot be replaced!

When you take over the wheel, the man you relieve will give you position and course, and you must repeat them after him so he can be sure that you hear and understand what he says. There is no legal form for conveying this information, but here is one that is usable: "We are in A strait, passed B lighthouse at 19:33, course is southwest by west one-half west. She has been making close to 9.5 knots on my watch." You must repeat what you hear in order to guarantee that you received the information correctly. If the skipper should give orders for a change of course, be sure to repeat them after him, always.

There will be a logbook in the pilothouse. On inside runs, keep the logbook up to date! Write down each point of reference, the exact time of having it abeam, and the course up to the next point of reference. Don't erase! There must be no erasures in the logbook; an erasure will discredit the logbook so that it may not be accepted as evidence in a court of law. If you do happen to make a mistake, draw a straight thin line through the entry (so that it still can be read), then rewrite on the next line below. Make certain that each entry in your logbook is correct; erroneous information is worse than no information at all.

Eyes front! Keep a sharp lookout, especially when on inside waters.

Most fishing vessels have an automatic steering machine on board. It was nicknamed "Iron Mike" years ago, and remains so named to this very day. Mike is indeed a great labor saver and an excellent helmsman, who will steer a straighter course than any human hands. Still, Mike has his shortcomings. For one thing, Mike does not know how to think for himself and must depend on you to do the thinking for him; he does not hear the order to change course, so you must hear it for him. For another thing, Mike is unable to look up ahead, so he must depend on your eyes.

Learn how to operate the Iron Mike. Several systems of automatic steering are in use, and they are not alike in every respect. On some types one must disengage the clutch when altering course; on other types not. Become familiar with the one you have on board so that you will be able to change course on short notice.

Iron Mike keeps your vessel on its course for you, which leaves you free to devote your full attention to looking ahead. A sharp scrutiny of the waters right in front of your bow is very important. Every one of the 900-odd nautical miles between Puget Sound and Cape Spencer is richly endowed with driftwood: logs, large and small, and much other debris that can do great damage to your propeller and propeller shaft if given the chance. North of Petersburg, Alaska, you may well meet small flotillas of icebergs, too many of which are large enough to sink your boat in the event of a collision.

Learn to "box the compass" — that is, to read the compass rose by points, half points, and quarter points. Some skippers (and mates) give courses in degrees, but a good many still use the point system. In any event, a sea-faring man must know how to receive orders either way, hence he must know the art of boxing the compass.

Do not read on your wheel watch! In recent years — since

the Iron Mike has been pressed into service as helmsman — such monstrous recklessness with other peoples' lives and property has been practiced on certain fishing vessels, sometimes with the skipper's permission, one hears! Be that as it may, the fact remains that a man who will read a story while he is supposed to be on lookout, and indeed is responsible for the safety of vessel and crew, is unfit to be in a pilothouse; and the skipper who gives his consent to such reckless behavior is unfit to be in command of a vessel of any size.

When running at night, step outside the pilothouse once or twice on your watch, especially if you see the running lights of an on-coming vessel up ahead, and make sure that your running lights are burning. A burnt-out bulb in one of your running lights can easily be the cause of a collision, especially on inside waters.

If you have to travel inside waters during the gillnet season, you will more than likely have to travel through waters where dozens, even hundreds, of gillnet boats are fishing. Here you must be extra, extra careful; here it is not only a question of looking ahead and seeing all those lights, it is also a question of judgment, of trying to decide for yourself which light represents the gillnet boat and which one the tail end of the gillnet! And even worse, which taillight belongs to which boat? On the bridge, in the pilothouse, or on a larger fishing vessel, your eyes will be some twelve to twenty feet above the water line; from that height it can be extremely difficult to judge the difference in height between the stern light on a gillnet boat and the light on the tail end of the net. A sharp lookout, coupled with a wide-awake watchfulness, is of the essence! If ever in doubt, call the skipper and ask his advice; you will get his help, too, of he thinks that you need it.

If you do run across a gillnet, now is the time your ability to quickly throttle down your engine and disengage your clutch will be of utmost importance to you. Do not try to back up! A gillnet in the propeller is something to be feared like the plague; for one thing, the net may be greatly damaged, causing loss of fishing time and perhaps an appearance in a court of law for yourself and your skipper. For another thing, your own vessel can be disabled, and have to call for a tow. One cannot run very far with any amount of gillnet web and lines wrapped around the propeller. Furthermore, nylon web and lines, or lines of any artificial fiber for that matter, will do damage to the propeller shaft and stern bearing if that fiber is wrapped in the propeller and the propeller is kept turning for any length of time. Moral: Don't get a gillnet in your propeller!

Show decent respect for and courtesy to your skipper. That does not mean that you should be obsequious, or crawling; it does mean that you owe the skipper the respect of a novice for an expert, of a follower for his chosen leader. Remember, the skipper is your leader in your work as well as in your general living while you are on board his vessel; he is also the expert upon whose knowledge and skill your earnings depend, and your safe return to dry land as well.

Leave the electronic instruments (sounders, radar, loran, ship-to-shore telephone, R.D.F., etc.) completely alone! Except upon orders from the skipper, of course. The instruments belong to the vessel, not to the crew, and the skipper (not you!) is responsible for their use. If the skipper wishes you to use any of them he will tell you so, and instruct you.

Do not help yourself to the charts and/or other navigational equipment; they are the property of the skipper. If he thinks it desirable or necessary that you consult a chart, he will show you the one in question. On the other hand, if you have a genuine thirst for knowledge, you should of course ask the skipper if he will be good enough to show you a certain chart and instruct you on how to read it.

Don't get into the habit of cluttering up the compass shelf with things that don't belong there; most skippers take a dim view of that particular type of disorder. Any object made of iron or steel (a tin can, knife, splicer, etc.) must be kept at least three feet away from the compass in order not to corrupt the compass needle. Photographic light meters and cameras with built-in light meters must also be kept at least three feet away from the compass; the same is true of flashlights. In short, keep the compass shelf uncluttered.

When your wheel watch is over, and the next man comes to take the watch, remember to give him course and position; don't force him to ask you for it! See that he repeats the information back to you correctly.

Was your relief prompt, did he appear in the pilothouse on time, or was he five minutes behind the clock? By the way, did *you* take over the wheel on the stroke of the hour, or were you a few minutes late? Remember, your trick at the wheel starts on the stroke of the hour, not five or six or ten minutes after. Be on time!

If you have fish in the boat, be sure to pump out the fish hold before going below. All fishing vessels have a hand-operated pump on deck; many boats have one or more pumps installed in the engine room. These may be electrically or mechanically driven, and may, on some vessels, be started from the pilothouse.

If you use the hand-operated deck pump for pumping out the hold, count the strokes each time you pump. This will tell you whether or not the ice is melting normally; an unusually large number of strokes will warn you that your vessel may be taking in water, that a small leak has developed somewhere below the water line, in the hull or in the stern bearing.

The deck pump may have to be primed in order to pick up the water from the bilge. Use the draw bucket; a single bucketful will do the trick.

If you use a power-driven pump, look at your watch when you start the pump, and again when you stop it. If you find that water in the bilges appears to be on the increase, notify the skipper at once.

CHAPTER 5

Working on Deck

IN COMMERCIAL fishing, the work of handling the various types of fishing gear is almost always teamwork. In the purse-seine, beach-seine, lampara-seine, as well as in the otter-trawl fisheries, the entire crew works as a team; in longlining, two men work as a team most of the time.

On a longline vessel a new man will always have as his partner or teammate an experienced man whose job it is to break in the beginner, teach him the tricks of the trade, and do whatever must be done in order to transform the greenhorn into a competent deep-sea fisherman. During this period of learning it is the beginner's bounden duty to do his best to learn as fast as he can, and to obey orders from his partner without arguments or back talk. Remember, while you are learning, you will not be able to do your share of the work—and it is your partner who must take up the slack when you fall behind!

To put into print a detailed description of how to work on deck would be a rank presumption; further, it would be an utterly useless undertaking, because each and every skipper has his own ideas as to how he wants work performed on board his vessel; besides that, every experienced fisherman who takes it upon himself to break in a green man has his own ideas on how to go about that task. Hence, a detailed description on a printed page will do but little good.

There are, however, some fundamental facts that will

serve as guidelines for the budding fisherman; we'll give a brief mention of some of the more important ones, starting by enumerating a few do's, then some don'ts.

Safety first, always — and that means safety of others as well as yourself. Look out so that you don't get hurt or cause a shipmate to get hurt!

Get out of your bunk the moment you are called. Don't be the last man to get on deck. Be the first on deck as often as possible.

When pulling and hauling as part of a team, make sure that you pull and haul your share of the load. Yes, and a wee bit more, too, if you can. "Pull hard, and it comes easy" is more than just a saying.

For instance, when stacking down a purse seine, be sure that you have as much of the web between your fists as your working partners on the seine table have between theirs. Watch your working partners' handwork (and footwork!) and learn to work in concert with them.

When some small but unpleasant job is to be done, and you think you have the know-how, do it! Your shipmates are doing part of your work for you while you are learning, and will continue to do so until you have learned to be as proficient in your work as they are; show them that you understand that and appreciate it.

Learn to handle deck machinery and to operate it with care so that you don't hurt yourself — or abuse the machinery. The different pieces of deck machinery are the tools needed for the performance of your work; it is part of good seamanship to avoid abuse of these tools and to help keep them in good working order. Be careful when using the wash-down water hose so that you don't throw a kink in it when moving along the deck. A sharp kink in the hose may well cause breakage of the water pump because of back pressures.

Keep your vessel clean! Hose down the deck as soon as you notice even a small accumulation of trash; a dirty deck is a dangerous deck, and many a man has taken a bad fall and hurt his back, knocked a hole in his scalp, or toppled overboard because he stepped on a blade of slippery kelp, a piece of gurdy bait, or a small flatfish just as the boat made an unexpected roll. It takes only a minute to hose down the deck, and it is a minute well spent, for reasons of both comfort and safety. A hosing-down is always in order; on the stern of a longline boat frequent hosing is of the utmost importance, because pieces of old bait will be strewn around when men are trying to bait in a hurry. A dirty deck is dangerous; keep your deck clean—the fellow you save from going overboard may be yourself!

Find your sea legs as quickly as you can; a goodly share of both your comfort and your safety depends upon how well you can stand on your feet when the boat is pitching and rolling. It has been estimated that, on the average, a commercial fisherman must use about one-third of his strength just to keep himself in an upright position. That's a man with sea legs, mind you. Before you find your sea legs you may have to use up as much as one-half your strength keeping yourself in a vertical position, even in a most moderate sea; in somewhat rough fishing weather you may well have to use most of your strength for that purpose — which will leave you with little strength for your work.

Keep your head covered when working on deck! This rule applies to everyone, only more so to those with long hair. Fish slime and fish gurry — the partly digested foodstuff in the guts of the fish — contain irritants that may cause a most unpleasant itch (and perhaps permanent damage) in your scalp. When stacking a purse seine or retrieving a trawl net, wear your sou'wester. Small particles of jellyfish will be fairly raining down upon you from the net; they are unpleasant and potentially dangerous to your eyes, skin, and scalp. Uncovered long hair may easily get caught in running tackle, drive belts and chains, gears, sprockets, etc. Don't take foolish chances; wear a sou'wester or other suitable head covering.

That much for the do's; now let's have a go at some don'ts. Don't step on or inside a coil of rope such as a purse line, buoy lines, or warps (wire ropes) while gear is being set out.

Such a step could provide you with a quick trip overboard, plus a broken leg or a mangled foot, or both!

Don't lay hold of running gear, longlines, buoy lines, warps, and the like outside the roller or line puller. Broken arms and mangled hands will be the result of such foolishness. If you must work on gear outside the roller or line puller, be sure that the gurdy or line puller has come to a complete stop before you lay hold of that gear!

Don't neglect to wear gloves when handling fishing gear. If you are dealing with wire rope, wear leather gloves. Your hide is easily punctured — and remember, most infections develop from small punctures.

Don't stand aft of the warp leading from the block at the railing to the winch drum when hauling in the trawl warps. If the wire rope should break, its whipping end can hit you — and divide you into halves.

Don't try to fair-lead a wire rope, whether warp or anchor cable, onto the winch drum by pushing on it with your hands or your feet! If the winch is not equipped with proper fair-leads, use an iron rod, a length of pipe, or a hardwood pole for guiding the wire rope onto the drum. Then be sure that you have good, solid footing, because a fall across the incoming warp could result in your being carried into the winch.

Don't step on the tackle as it comes down on deck from the gypsy head. Instead, throw the tackle rope away from you, so that it is clear of your feet.

Don't put too many turns on the gypsy head when using an old-fashioned deck (purse) winch. Just one turn too many can cause overlap; if this should happen to you, stop the winch at once and call for someone to give you a hand clearing the tackle.

It is not good practice for one man to try using the gypsy head for pulling line *and also* manning the start-stop controls, even if they are close by. If you get entangled in the line, you may not be able to reach the controls. Keep this in mind.

CHAPTER 6

The Tools of the Trade

COMMERCIAL fishing has gone through a head-over-heels development during these last two decades and is no longer a "simple" occupation. Quite the contrary, commercial fishing is an occupation that demands both knowledge and ability.

This does not mean, however, that a man must have a degree from a college or a university or any other institution of learning before he can "go fishin'." That kind of knowledge may be required later on, perhaps. But not to begin with; so let's take first things first.

The first thing a would-be fisherman must learn is to build and repair fishing gear. When a man has learned this first lesson well, he will find it easy enough to get a "chance" — a berth — on a fishing vessel, and start his career as a commercial fisherman.

If a trawl net is used, the beginning fisherman must learn how to build such a net, because a trawl net, being tapered from wide in the upper end to very narrow in the lower end, is made up of many pieces of web, each one cut to its own peculiar pattern. Such cuts are called *tapers*, and tapers vary from one type of trawl net to another, and from one part of the net to another part of the same net, as well. And, when a trawl net is torn, which it frequently is, one or more of the tapered pieces of web may be so badly damaged that it must be removed from the net and replaced with a new piece, which, of course, must be cut to exactly the same pattern.

Hence, having the know-how to cut a taper is important for a trawl fisherman.

Once a man has learned his web work, and is able to do the maintenance work on a trawl net, he will have no difficulty in keeping up with the work on seines or gillnets — all of which is rather uncomplicated, compared to the web work on a trawl net.

Next, the would-be fisherman should have a working knowledge of *marlinspike seamanship*: how to make the knots commonly used in the fishing trades and how to splice fiber rope and wire rope. Having learned such work, he will quickly catch on to the tricks in rigging longlines, buoy lines, and warps, and in making and rigging pots for lobster, shrimp, crab, or whatever kind of creature he may want to catch. And will thus have no trouble finding a berth on board a fishing vessel.

When a young man has been a fisherman before the mast for a few years, and has learned a good many tricks of the fishing trade, he may decide that he wants to make fishing his life work, that he wants to own and operate his own fishing vessel. Such a man must then equip himself with a goodly portion of special knowledge in several different fields. He must know not only where to look for the fish he wants to catch, but he must also know enough of the science of navigation to get to where he expects the fish to be schooling up. He must know enough about his diesel engine to be able to spot potential trouble before it has had the chance to develop into a full-grown problem. He should have a fairly good understanding of hydraulics and of electronics, for the same reason. Even the very best of machinery, the finest of instruments, must still be operated by a *man*. It is important that the man in question know enough about the machinery and about the instrument to handle it correctly.

Right now, however, we are speaking about beginners; there is a long, long road to travel from that first strange day on the deck of a fishing vessel to the responsible and commanding position on the bridge. Again, let's take first things first. And the first — the very first — thing a would-be skipper must learn is to build, repair, and handle fishing gear — the tools of his trade.

There are two basic instruments used for catching fish: namely, the *hook* and the *net*. No one person, or tribe of persons, may lay claim to being their inventor or inventors; both the fishhook and the fishnet were, of course, developed over a very long period of time. All we really know of their past history is that they have been in use for several thousand years in widely separated parts of the world.

There are many variations of each of these two basic implements, and more than 90 percent of all the fish caught in the world today is taken by means of either a hook or a net of some kind. A method of catching fish by means of an electric current coupled with a powerful pump has been invented and tested in Germany, but the cost of making such fishing operations safe in saltwater is so high that this method may be said to be impractical at this time. What may happen to this invention in the years to come may be a different matter.

The fishhook is used in various commercial fisheries such as jigging (in the albacore fishery), trolling, longlining, and hand-lining. In Pacific Northwest waters it is used in jigging, trolling, and longlining only, there being no commercial hand-line fishery on that coast.

Fishnets are made from netting—commonly called *web* in the fishing industry. From netting, or web, one can make a

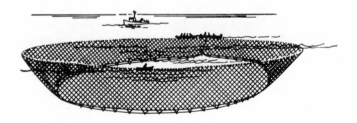

PURSE SEINE

great many different kinds of nets. You may be familiar with some of them, such as gillnets and seines, both of which are commonly used in the Pacific Northwest.

Seines are often referred to as an *encircling* type of gear, because we sink the net down around or behind a school of fish: we *encircle* the school. In the case of the *purse seine*, we encircle the fish and close the bottom of the seine by means of the purse line, thereby trapping the fish. The *beach seine* is set out in a half-circle, or horse-shoe shape, behind the school of fish; both ends of the net are then pulled in onto the beach, thus trapping the fish between the net and the beach.

Gillnets are referred to as an *enmeshing* type of gear; when a fish hits the net, its head will go through the mesh; the mesh will lodge behind the gill covers, trapping the fish. Thus the fish is said to be *enmeshed* in the net. In the Pacific Northwest, floating gillnets only (mostly drift nets) are used. In other parts of the world, standing, or bottom, gillnets are widely used, especially in the cod, saithe, herring, and plaice fisheries. In the Pacific Northwest such bottom gillnets were in use during the "soupfin shark era," in the middle 1940's. It is quite possible that such a system of fishing might be put to profitable use even today, particularly in certain parts of Alaska.

Web is a most versatile agent, and may be made into a great variety of nets such as the *purse seine, Danish seine (snurrevod), lampara seine, beach seine, gillnet, trammel net, cast net, hoop net, flyke net,* and, last but not least, *trawl net* — of which a great many types have been made, and of which many more types will be made in years to come.

The modern trawl is probably the most efficient piece of fishing gear in commercial use today. It is employed in a number of different fisheries in all parts of the fishing world, particularly by the big fishing nations, and will no doubt be still more widely and intensively used in future years. A young man of today who plans to make his living as a commercial fisherman will be wise to try to learn everything— that is, as much as possible—about the trawl, because he will most likely be using some type of trawl sooner or later.

In the Pacific Northwest most people regard the trawl as a 'new" or "modern" method of fishing. The fact is that the trawl is not new at all. Quite the contrary, the trawl is a rather old piece of equipment. We do not know just *how* old; neither do we know where the trawl originated, but we do know that a form of trawl was operated on the coasts of the British Isles more than six hundred years ago. It was a very simple type of trawl, to be sure, this first "bottom dragnet." It was called a *wondyrchoun* — whatever that may mean — and it was fished mainly by the force of the tidal current. The fishermen rowed or sailed a piece out to sea with the ebb tide, set the net down to the bottom, and let the incoming tide do the work of towing. When they had drifted in on reasonably shallow water they pulled in their wondyrchoun —which was now pretty well filled with fish.

In the year 1377 the British Commons complained to the king about "that terrible instrument, the wondyrchoun, which caught a great many fishes, to the destruction of the fisheries" (which tells us that there were gear fights among the commercial fishermen even in those far-away days!). The complaint to the king stated, further, that "this was a 'layzie and idle kynde' of fishing, because these fishermen filled their boats with fish in a few hours, then came in and sold their catch at good prices in the early morning, after which they spent the rest of the day drinking strong ale in the public houses!"

The king listened to the complaint and issued a proclamation outlawing the wondyrchoun — the trawl. And so the trawl was, supposedly, legally dead. The only trouble was that the trawl refused to stay dead. It popped up again, bigger and better than ever. This went on for three hundred years, and more; the king would issue a proclamation killing the trawl; trawler men were rounded up and tucked away in jail, and their nets were confiscated and burnt. Still the trawl came back, again and again, until, finally, the king became tired of issuing proclamations. And so, at the beginning of the 1800's, the trawl was in use all along the coast of Great Britain.

The early deep-sea trawling was done by sailing vessels, and the net was called a beam trawl, with the mouth, or the business end of the net, kept open by means of a timber or beam. This trawl was towed by a single warp, which, of course, was hauled by men manning the capstan; there was no power with which to perform that kind of labor in those days.

When power — first the steam, later the internal-combustion, engine—came into the fishing fleet, the trawl fishery made a mighty leap forward. Bigger and heavier nets could be used, and the fishing vessels could cover many more and far-away fishing grounds; trawling very quickly became by far the most efficient method of catching several species of bottom fish. Then the *otter boards* came into being, and this invention enabled the trawler men to use still larger nets and also to fish in far rougher weather than could be done with the beam trawl. England was the pioneer in the deep-sea trawl fishery, but other nations — Germany, France, and Poland — soon joined in. In recent years all leading fishing nations have acquired large and very efficient trawl fleets; today trawlers from Japan, Russia, Iceland, and Norway are roaming the seven seas.

We may, roughly, divide the trawl net into three main groups, namely the *beam trawl*, the *otter trawl*, and the *pelagic*, or *midwater*, *trawl*. Within each of these three groups there are in turn trawls of different sizes and shapes, depending upon what kind of fish one wants to catch, on the size and power of the fishing vessel, on what kind of sea bottom one is operating on, and so forth.

THE BEAM TRAWL

The beam trawl is the simplest type of trawl and does not, in fact, look so very different from that wondyrchoun used in England more than six hundred years ago. A beam trawl consists of a shallow, baglike net, a long wooden *beam* as long as the net is wide — and two *runners* made of heavy, flat iron and shaped, roughly, like the capital letter "D." (The runners are also called *shoes* or *trawl heads*, in different places.) In the United States and Canada the beam trawl has been in retirement for a good many years, by and large, and is at this time used only in the Petersburg-Wrangell district in Alaska in the local shrimp fishery.

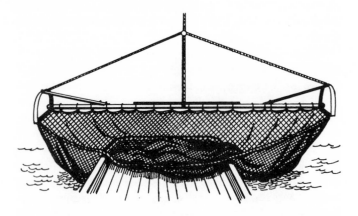

BEAM TRAWL

The beam trawls used in Alaska today have a beam about fifty feet long. The ends of the beam are bolted onto the top side of the runners. The upper (top) edge of the net is straight and is lashed onto the beam evenly from one runner to the other. On the bottom of the net, the web has been cut back a bit so that the lead line—called the *foot rope*—will form a semicircle, and drag the ocean floor a few feet behind the beam. A beam trawl is pulled by a single warp of wire rope at slow speed — about one to two knots.

OTTER TRAWLS

Whereas the beam trawl is kept in fishing position by means of a beam, the otter trawl is kept open by means of *otter boards*, two large door-shaped boards commonly called *trawl doors*. They come in many sizes and shapes; a door about eight feet long and five feet wide is as a rule adequate for the size of net used on the Pacific Northwest coast. A larger net will require a bigger and heavier door. On smaller

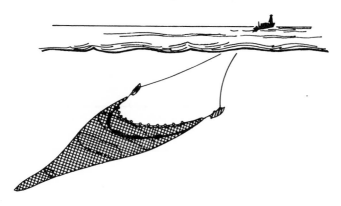

OTTER TRAWL (SHRIMP)

nets, such as the shrimp trawls used in the Gulf of Mexico, smaller and lighter doors are commonly used. Trawl skippers have their own ideas as to the best size and weight of the doors, and such ideas differ sometimes to a rather high degree. The V door, invented in Taiwan about twenty years ago, seems to be superior to the old type of flat door, and is much used in the Pacific trawl fleet.

On an otter trawl, the mouth of the net is connected to the otter boards, or doors, by means of four wire rope cables, two for each door — one from the top rope and the other from the foot rope of the net. These cables are named *dande lines*, and may be from five to fifty fathoms long, depending upon what kind of net is used, what kind of fish sought, and the personal preference of the skipper. In shrimp trawling, Gulf of Mexico style, the ears (ends) of the head rope and the foot rope are connected directly onto the otter board, with no dande lines in between.

In the Pacific Coast trawl fisheries, an otter trawl is generally towed by two warps, one on each side of the vessel. The towing warp is connected to the otter board on the opposite side from where the dande lines are fastened, and at a different point of stress. When the vessel moves ahead, taking strain on the warps, the net exerts strain in the opposite direction, and the otter boards are forced to shear out. The doors will stretch the net between them and keep the mouth of the net open.

An otter-trawl net is shaped more or less as an immensely big bag, wide in the forward end and tapering gradually to the narrow tail end which is called the *cod end*. The net is made up of several sections, such as the *wings*, which connect to the dande lines, and the *body*, also called the *throat*. The wings and body form the top and bottom sections of the net. Some nets also have *side panels*, which are part of the body. Behind the body comes the *intermediate*, a long straight tube of web, running from the narrow part of the body to the fish-bag, or cod end, which is the *bitter end* of the trawl net.

Trawl nets come in many sizes; a shrimp-trawl net may be anywhere from 42 feet to 100 feet or more across its mouth; ground-fish trawls commonly used in the Pacific Northwest trawl fishery are generally 95 to 105 feet wide and are capable of taking quite large hauls: catches of forty thousand pounds per tow have been reported.

Basic design of the otter trawl has changed but little during the past twenty-five to thirty years. Nets have grown larger as fishing vessels have acquired more horsepower and so can pull larger nets at an adequate rate of speed; basically, however, the otter-trawl net is much the same today as it was about a generation ago.

THE PELAGIC TRAWL

The pelagic, or midwater, trawl also is an otter trawl insofar as it is kept open by means of otter boards or doors. The real difference between a pelagic trawl and an ordinary otter trawl is that the usual otter trawl is designed to follow the ocean floor while a pelagic trawl may be made to travel anywhere between the surface and the bottom of the sea. This is accomplished by various means such as using a special type of otter boards, hooking the net onto the boards in a different manner, adjusting the length of the warps, regulating towing speed, or by using a combination of two or more of these means. A telemeter system which shows the exact depth at which the trawl is fishing is often used with the pelagic trawl.

A very large net, the pelagic trawl is best used from a larger vessel, that is, a vessel large enough to mount a large net reel on its stern and provide horsepower enough to tow the net at required speeds. In design, the pelagic trawl differs from the bottom-fish trawl in that the pelagic trawl has four equally large "sides": the top, the bottom, and the two side panels are all of a size. The pelagic trawl here referred to is called the *Cobb pelagic trawl*, since it was developed on board the N.M.F.S. research vessel *John N. Cobb* of Seattle, Washington.

LONGLINES

Longlining is the oldest deep-sea fishery in the Pacific Northwest, and was indeed the only one up to the advent of deep-sea trawling in the early 1940's.

A *longline* is just what the name implies: a long line, called the *groundline*, onto which a certain number of hooks have been attached. The distance between hooks, as well as the size of the hooks, varies, depending upon what kind of fish one is trying to catch, abundance of fish on the grounds, and, in some cases, on the method of hauling used on board the vessel.

Hooks are connected to the groundline by means of short lines called *gangions* on the Pacific Coast or *snoods* in Great Britain and in some parts of the eastern United States. Gangions — or snoods — are, in effect, what would be termed a *leader* on a hand line or on a sport-fisherman's reel. Gangions vary in length and in breaking strength according to the type of longline, method of setting and hauling, and species of fish sought.

In the Pacific Northwest, longlines are used in the halibut and in the sablefish fisheries only. Lines are generally rigged from ¼-inch-diameter laid rope; from nylon, orlon, or dacron; or from a mixture of two or more artificial fiber ropes now on the market; breaking strength of modern halibut longlines may vary from 1250 to some 1700 pounds. Gangions are made from braided nylon line of 250 to 300 pounds' breaking strength.

Gangions are attached to the groundline by means of *beckets*, small loops of heavy twine stuck in between the strands of the line and secured by an overhand bend. (The *sticking-in* of the becket probably gave the expression "sticking the gear" to the rigging of longlines. The term has been in use in the fishing fleet for generations, and is still used in the longline fleet.)

Length of gangions varies according to the fishery; on halibut lines, gangions generally run 48 to 52 inches in length, while lines used exclusively for sablefish (black cod) carry shorter gangions.

Longlines are spoken of as 9-foot gear, 13-foot gear, 18-foot gear, and so on, according to distance between the hooks. Lines with 9 feet or less between hooks are said to be *short-set gear*, while lines with 18 or more feet between hooks will be called *long-set gear*. In the sablefish fishery, short-set gear is considered to be the most effective, and some of the sablefish boats use 3-foot gear — hooks spaced only 3 feet apart. On such gear, gangions have to be correspondingly shortened in order to avoid too many snarls on the lines. Halibut lines may have as little as 13 feet or as much as 24 feet between hooks, depending upon what measure the skipper considers to be the best.

Longlines are sometimes used as *pelagic gear*, the groundline being kept floating just below the surface of the water by means of small floats. Floating longlines are widely used in the tuna fisheries and in some shark fisheries, in the waters fished by the Japanese, in the South Pacific Ocean, and in the Indian Ocean. In Sweden and Denmark, floating longlines are to some extent employed in the salmon fisheries.

Halibut and sablefish longlines are generally made up — "stuck" — in units called *skates*; when hauled, each skate is coiled down on deck as it is taken in by the gurdy, each hook being placed in a certain position within the skate by the *coiler* — the fisherman whose turn it is to coil the gear. After having been rebaited, the skate is set out through a chute located on the very tip of the vessel's stern. Several skates are joined together by a simple knot to form a *string*, referred to as *a string o' gear*, or a *set*. A halibut vessel may operate with several such strings in the water, each of which may consist of as many as 10 skates. A *skate o' gear* is usually 300 fathoms long and may carry as many as 192 hooks if short-set, or as few as 75 if long-set.

Use of *tub gear* is another method of baiting and setting out longlines. The lines are coiled down into a wooden or plastic tub, and the point of each hook is stuck lightly, in sequence, into the rim of the tub. When gear is made ready for setting, the hooks are loosened, baited, and hung side by side outside of the tub, with the lines remaining coiled inside. A shorter gangion — 30 to 36 inches — is preferred for easier handling.

Tub gear cannot be set out through a chute; such gear is set out by hand, with the help of a stick 2 to 3 feet long. One end of the stick is placed underneath the line; a quick lifting-and-throwing motion of the stick will cause several fathoms of line to run out of the tub, taking the hooks along without bringing them into contact with one another. Tub gear can be set out at a rather good clip, although not as fast as gear set through a chute. Coiling the lines back into the tub, however, is rather simple work and does not require nearly as much skill or training as is necessary for coiling lines into a skate. Tub gear is therefore often used on one- or two-man boats, or by men who have no special training in the longline fisheries.

CHAPTER 7

About Marlinspike Seamanship

THE term *marlinspike seamanship* covers all work where a marlinspike comes into play, and covers a good deal more as well. A marlinspike is a tapered spike, anywhere from 6 inches to 2 or 3 feet in length, made from reasonably good quality steel; it has a *head* somewhat like the head of a carriage bolt on its heavy end. Its shank is smooth, its point, sharp; it will slide in and through a man's hand or leg real fast and easy if the man who uses it is careless. In the fishing fleet, a marlinspike is seldom used except for splicing wire rope.

Fishermen use two other implements for splicing ropes and lines. The first is a short steel or brass spike with a wooden handle or head. It is called a *splicer*, and is used for sticking halibut gear (longlines) and for splicing *small stuff* — lines and ropes up to ½ inch in diameter. The second splicing implement is called a *fid*. Made of hardwood (ash, iron bark, etc.) the fid is tapered more sharply than the marlinspike and the splicer. Fids come in various sizes: most commonly used are fids 10 to 12 inches long, for ropes ½ to 1½ inches in diameter, and 14 to 18 inches long, for heavier ropes.

Practically all web, twines, lines, and ropes used in today's commercial fishing operations are made from synthetic fibers. A number of such fibers is now on the market; all of them are, practically speaking, rotproof. In addition, ropes made from some of these fibers may have a greater tensile strength than those made from other fibers such as cotton, manila, or sisal. A manila rope 1 inch in diameter has a tensile strength of 9,000 pounds, while cotton rope of the same diameter has a strength of only 5,100 pounds. By comparison, a 1-inch-diameter synthetic-fiber rope has a tensile strength of from 12,600 pounds (polyethylene) to 24,000 pounds (nylon).

These are "approximate averages," says the manufacturer. Bear in mind that the tensile strength of four-stranded, of extra-hard-laid, and of extra-soft-laid ropes will also vary slightly from the above approximations.

Handling and Care

Modern ropes are very good; they are also very expensive, and deserving of proper handling and care so that they will last a long time and give service corresponding to their cost.

"Ah, but it is the vessel, not I, that pays the cost of the ropes," you might say. True, the vessel does pay. Actually, this truth is only superficial, for in the final accounting, it is the *catch* that must pay for the ropes. The vessel must pay its rope bill out of its share of the catch; thus, as the bill grows larger, so must the vessel's share of the catch grow larger. Which means, quite simply, that *your* share of the catch must be proportionally smaller. Therefore, taking good care of fishing gear, ropes included, is just plain common sense and good economy all around.

When uncoiling a new coil of rope, lay the coil flat on deck, *inside rope-end down*. Cut the lashings and pull the inside end up through the center. Right-layed rope uncoils in a counterclockwise direction.

Dirt — such as sand, mud, and clay — that gets in between strands of rope will act as an abrasive and cut the fine threads in the strands. So, obviously, a clean rope will give longer service than will a dirty one. A thorough washing with a high-pressure water hose will remove most of the abrasive materials and help keep the rope strong and make it last longer.

Ropes should be coiled down clockwise — "with the sun."

An exception to this rule is braided rope, which is better coiled in a figure eight. After use, hang rope up on a peg or on a belaying pin, or tie it to a shroud or whatever, so that your rope can get plenty of air; let it dry out before it is stowed away.

Sharp-angled objects, such as encountered when a rope is used as a sling, will put undue strain on the outer fibers of the rope. So will knots; do not knot two rope ends together except in an emergency. Take time to make a short splice — provided that a long splice is not called for.

When splicing, remember that ropes of synthetic materials are very slick and slippery. Also, such rope has very little shrinkage or none at all; hence, the splice will not tighten up when it gets wet as will a splice on a manila or cotton rope. Therefore, it is necessary to use a larger number of tucks when splicing rope of synthetic fiber. An eye splice in a cotton/manila rope will hold all right with four tucks; it is good practice to double the number of tucks when splicing synthetic ropes — more, if rope is extra-soft-laid.

Do not overload your rope. Generally speaking, a load of one-fifth — 20 percent — of the rope's breaking strength is considered a "safe" load.

CHAPTER 8

Responsibilities

THE crewman of a fishing boat has other responsibilities besides being a fisherman, knowing about gear, and standing watch. He is also a seaman. This means that if a coil of line drops from the shrouds, you coil it back in place. It is not left to the other fellow. Running rigging is not tied to the belaying pins but is hauled tight and passed several turns on the belaying pins, then a hitch made to hold it in place. The balance of the line should be coiled in the rigging and the end passed around, and, with a couple of hitches, tied into a neat bundle.

Keep an eye about you for rigging that is chafed, is rubbing against a stay and will get chafed, or is slack when it should be tight. With modern synthetic lines, running rigging generally remains taut. In the days of manila and hemp it was routine to slack rigging when it got wet and to take it up snug again after a dry spell, because vegetable fibers absorbed moisture and swelled, shrinking such rope in length. At times rigging got so tight that some of its strands came apart.

Besides general responsibilities of caring and accounting for your share of the fishing gear, you may, as time goes on, be elected as a representative of the crew, or take on the job of being the cook or the chief (the engineer). By that time you will know what knowledge these men need, and the responsibilities they have. The delegate is often a deck boss, who may oversee the maintenance of the gear, besides

sitting with the skipper and going over the bills before a settlement. If there is a union, he is its representative. Even when
there is not a union, there is generally a group leader on
deck through the tacit understanding of skipper and crew.

The cook and the chief have their separate domains of
responsibility and prerogatives, and a privileged relation-
ship with others. Observe these; they will not be posted as a
watch bill of do's and don'ts in the galley or fo'c'sle.

The simple act of making fast to another boat or to the
dock, or of letting go, though it seems so smooth and effort-
less, is also an act of seamanship. In time you will note the
habits (and shortcomings) of the skipper's style in coming
alongside the dock or another boat and the sequence usually
followed when letting go. Anticipate the need for fenders
over the side, and know where they go and how far to let
them down. Only under very special circumstances will the
stern line be made fast before the bow line. Learn to check
the way of the boat smoothly, keeping your hands clear.

God help the man who takes a turn on the cleat with a knot
first! With a severe strain on modern nylon line, cutting the
line is the only alternative out of that dilemma. Put turns
only on a deck cleat, no hitches.

Know about the use of spring lines and how a boat can be
warped around the end of a dock or sprung out from the dock
so the vessel can back away without scraping the dock or an
adjoining boat. In close quarters, be ready to fend off from
another boat with the fender, and keep the skipper informed
of another boat that may suddenly move into the way out of
his line of vision.

In the Seattle area, most fishing vessels must transit a set
of locks, either when coming from sea or returning to sea.
Depending on tide level, the drop from the ship canal to sea
level varies from twelve to twenty-four feet. A ship tied to
the lock wall presents special problems that require constant
alertness when tending the lines.

When the water level in the locks is rising or falling, lines
must be taken in or let out constantly, and enough tension
maintained to keep the boat close to the wall, but without

parting the tie-up (or mooring) lines. Other complications are that water turbulence from the lock pumps makes the boat bounce around, and that sometimes the lock chambers are crowded with other boats.

The lock master gives the orders here — where to make fast, when to let go — but make certain the skipper also gets the message. These and others are skills that become second nature, are a set of understandings between you, your shipmates, and the skipper. In all aspects of operation, either around the dock or at sea fishing, one of the noteworthy characteristics of a well-run boat is the lack of orders, the lack of instructions that pass between skipper and crew. This characteristic has been noted by observant people many times when they first come aboard a fishing vessel.

Another job is to get stores aboard just before leaving town. Everyone helps carry the groceries aboard, but usually the cook puts them away. Taking on ice at the chute may involve only one or two men, more if bait also comes aboard. Memorize *exactly* where the bait goes in the hold and how much ice is stored in each side pen and the slaughterhouses.

When fish are being iced at sea, this has to be done in a particular sequence, since the hold is nearly full of ice and bait. Oh, the misery of work that results when too much ice is put in the wrong place! Whether there are ten tons or twenty tons of ice aboard, it will *all* have to be moved at least once, either with a scoop or a shovel, before the hold is full of iced fish. If there is a ton or two in the wrong place, that will have to be moved twice with a shovel and a sore back, and this does indeed make a man very observant when taking ice the next trip.

Lube oil, fuel, and water will be taken aboard at the fuel dock. Know which deck flange is for oil, which is for fresh water. You will be instructed by the chief or the skipper. Keep a sharp eye on the hose nozzle so that you don't overfill and find oil spouting all over the deck and yourself. Grease the deck flanges before screwing them back in place. Make them snug, but don't use a hammer on the flange wrench.

If oil is spilled on deck, clean it up. Ordinary dish-washing detergent is an excellent oil cleaner. Scrub in the detergent, then rinse off with a hose. Repeat if necessary.

Let's talk about that deck a little bit. It is both a working platform and a roof over your head in the fo'c'sle, the hold, and the engine room. Most fishing vessels still have wooden decks and caulked seams. You will also note that in most cases the decks are tarred or oiled for protection and preservation of the wood.

If a knife, a splicer, or other sharp instrument is stuck into the deck, this pierces the tar film and forms an entry for water, and possibly the beginnings of dry rot. If the deck is damaged by accident, let the skipper know so that he can treat it.

A fishing boat works in a running sea, and this may loosen the caulking in time. Also, in hot, dry weather the wood and caulking shrink, so that water may drip through below, sometimes onto your bunk. Eventually under wet conditions this will stop. If it doesn't, again let the skipper know.

CHAPTER 9

The Hold

You will get well acquainted with the fish hold in your boat, its arrangement, and the working practices therein. Each fishing boat's hold varies in size and arrangement, but some general statements are in order.

The fish hold is divided into *crossings* varying in number from three to six, depending on their size and on the species of fish carried.

A crossing is a transverse division from port to starboard, usually subdivided fore and aft into three compartments by *pen boards* that are inserted into *channel frames,* and when all pen boards are in place up to the deck, the hold is *penned up.*

Standing over the keel, in the middle of a crossing, is a square area called the *slaughterhouse*. At each side of the crossings where the bilge curves upward, is the *side pen*, sometimes called a *wing pen*.

In either the after or forward end of the fish hold, there is a pit covered with heavy boards that usually are notched or bored through with holes to permit drainage. This pit is called a *sump*. All melt water from the ice and fish drains to the sump and this has to be cleaned out last after washing the hold.

In the schooner-type vessel, the slaughterhouse floor is flat. But in a seine-type vessel with the engine forward, the propeller shaft passes through the fish hold with a shaft box generally built around it, possibly a foot or two high, running the length of the fish hold. The boards covering the shaft must be removed and washed, and the inside of the shaft box washed.

The fish are not butchered in the slaughterhouse; they are *dressed* (cleaned) up on deck, if at all. Possibly in the dim past of fishing, the name of the slaughterhouse may have had some connection with fish preparation.

When unloading fish, do not stand under the open hatch when a sling-load of fish is going up. The slings are strong enough, but often a single fish may slide out and give you a playful whack going by. The whack is a measure of the fish's weight multiplied by its velocity, and can be painful to say the least, and could break something in your upper parts.

Washing the hold after unloading is important to the quality of the next load of fish. Residual slime and blood must be scrubbed out of the boards and the corners of the cleats. Most vessels follow the last rinse with a spray of disinfectant. Here, as always, when you work with shipmates, do the best job of which you are capable. With most fishermen, it is an insult to have another go over the same surface or repeat the job someone else just completed. But at times it can happen that, rather than criticize another's job, fishermen will openly do it over again and communicate in that way their opinion of sloppy work.

Other instructions for particular jobs that need doing in the hold, such as cleaning sumps or opening the doors above the shelves in the skin of the boat, will be given to you. Each boat has its own peculiarities in these details. Once the instructions are understood, it should not be necessary to repeat them next trip.

CHAPTER 10

Your Medical Rights and Personal Care

A FISHERMAN is also a seaman; the fact is that a competent
deep-water fisherman is as good a seaman as may be found
anywhere.

As a seaman, the fisherman has a right to free medical care
in case of illness or injury. "Under a rule as old [as the
maritime law itself] a seaman injured or sick while under
articles is entitled to receive from the ship owner maintenance and cure: food, lodging, and care."*

Medically, the responsibility of the ship owner was long
ago erased by the federal government, and the seaman is
therefore entitled to free medical care, including hospitaliza-
tion, in a public health hospital (formerly called a marine
hospital). He is also entitled to "maintenance" — a given
sum of money per day — until his physician declares him
cured and fit for duty.

Canada does not operate marine hospitals; however, all
Canadians are eligible for hospital and medical coverage
under the cost-shared Federal/Provincial medical and hospital plans. Canadian seamen have this coverage, which can
be transferred from one province to another.

If and when you need medical help, you must first of all

*C. J. Simpson, "Federal Responsibilities for Medical Care of Seamen"
(Seattle, Trade Printery, 1955). Simpson is director of the National Labor
Bureau in San Francisco.

see your skipper, because the skipper or his representative must sign a document attesting that you are indeed employed on board a fishing vessel.

On longline vessels that belong to the Fishing Vessel Owners' Association and sail under an agreement with the Deep Sea Fishermen's Union, you are entitled to your full share of the trip on which you became ill or suffered an injury, regardless of whether you became unfit for work in the early part of the trip or near its end.

In any case, it is the duty of the skipper, and of the delegate if you have one on board, to inform a sick or injured fisherman of his rights and see that he gets what he is entitled to, including proper medical attention.

While on the subject of medical care, let's mention some things you can do to keep doctor and hospital away from you.

When at sea, take extra-good care of your health! You are not a sissy if you do; you are pretty much of a fool if you don't. Pay special attention to the care of your hands. Keep your hands clean, and don't let slime and gurry dry on your hands, because that will dry out your skin and cause cracks to develop. After washing your hands at the end of a long workday, use a good hand lotion or salve, working it well into the skin. A large tube of Johnson & Johnson Antiseptic First Aid Cream should be part of the standard outfit for a deepwater fisherman.

Beware of fish wounds! There are not any really poisonous fish on the western coast of North America, but there are fish such as the stingray (in California) and the ratfish (in all Pacific Northwest waters) that can be bad enough; a sting from either of these will bring you a powerful case of blood poisoning, if not promptly and properly treated.

The ratfish carries a "dagger" as part of its dorsal fin; if stuck by that one in your foot or in your hand, get yourself into the galley as fast as you can; fill a bucket with hot water, add a liberal amount of Clorox, Purex, or a drawing agent like Epsom Salts, and soak your limb in the solution. Keep the water as hot as you can take it. Keep soaking for at least two hours!

Sticks from sculpin, spiny dogfish, or any one of the twenty-odd rockfish found in Pacific Northwest waters may also be dangerous and should be treated as described. Do not neglect a small puncture of your hide! Remember, most infections originate in a small, insignificant scratch or sore.

CARE OF HANDS

The gnarled, calloused, knobby hands of an old-time fisherman were painfully acquired, but today such a mark of a vocation is no longer necessary or desirable. Hands do acquire callouses from sliding gear through them, and they get knobby and arthritic from long exposure to saltwater, but this is no longer much of a vocational affliction.

After several days of working with cloth gloves only, his hands wet from saltwater, fish slime, and blood, the fisherman awakes to another day with hands that are stiff, puffed up, and painful to move; any small cuts gape open as the skin is pulled taut from increased muscle tension caused by water saturation and swollen muscles. Buttoning the shirt is a slow, painful process. The quickest relief is to put on those soaking-wet gloves so the skin takes up water and softens again; squeezing and working the hands will, within twenty or thirty minutes, make them pliable and painless to work with.

About 1955, some fishermen experimented with a thin rubber surgical-type glove to be worn inside the cloth working glove. It was a successful experiment. Yes, the hands still get wet, but principally from natural skin moisture. And in the morning, the hands are not stiff and sore. Remarkably enough, small cuts now will heal while fishermen are still working on the fishing grounds. In the old days cuts in the hand chafed on the cloth gloves, and what started as a small skin cut would, in four or five days of fishing, grow to an open sore, the skin worn away at the edges. Bandages wouldn't stay in place.

The rubber surgical glove should not fit so tightly as to impede circulation in the fingers, but should be snug enough so that gear can be handled without the hands sliding about in the glove when wet, and without the sense of touch being too dulled by folds of rubber. Some fishermen prefer long gauntlets on the gloves that will cover their wrists and keep them dry.

Two pairs of rubber gloves will do the work of three pairs, since a left-hand glove can be turned inside out and become a right-hand glove, and vice versa. Even a glove with a torn finger will protect the hand, and can be used if you have no spares. You will note, though, that the finger in that torn part of the glove will have some soreness from saltwater exposure.

Take care of the rubber gloves by washing them clean inside and out at the end of the workday. Turn them inside out by rolling the gauntlet over the fingers and blowing up the glove like a balloon, with a sharp puff. When you awake in the morning, the outside will be dry. Reverse them again. They will slide on more easily if they are dusted lightly inside with talcum powder. Even cornmeal or ordinary flour will do the job, though it looks like pancake dough when you remove the gloves at the end of the day.

Good care of your hands is important to you *and* to your shipmates, because if you are crippled, the extra work falls on them, and this can slow the fishing and force the crew to work longer hours.

You are issued only one pair of hands. They are your livelihood. Watch the old-timer, who at the end of the day inspects his hands for unsuspected cuts. He carefully washes his hands, his wrists, and his arms. Blood and slime can clog pores and create rashes and pimples that turn into sores and become infected. From past experience, we can testify that almost 50 percent of the first-trippers have hand problems caused by neglect, as a result of their hurry to get to the bunk for those few short hours of sleep. (Being so short, it's more like a nap, or a "kink," as some old-timers express it.)

Some men annoint their hands with lotion or salve, and all treat their little cuts with tincture of Merthiolate, rubbing alcohol, or other good disinfectant. A few Band Aids in your kit will also be useful.

Penicillin tablets are by prescription only, and keep in mind that they are not to be used as a preventative, ever. Use them at the intervals prescribed only *after* you get an infection, and know whether you are allergic to penicillin.

When washing wristers or cloth gloves, rinse well to get the worst of the blood and slime out. As a finishing touch, many old-timers wring out lightly, then toss their gloves on deck and stamp hard on them with the heel of the boot, repeating this several times. This forces out all bacteria-laden slime and blood. Stamp on the end of the glove fingers first, though; glove fingers will pop like balloons if the water within is forced toward the fingers with the first stamp. Repeat the process until the water wrung out is clean.

CARE OF FEET

Not much can be added about foot care that has not already been said of the hands. Ill-fitting boots or socks that cause a slight discomfort initially can, by the end of several days, cause chafes and sores that are crippling. Few if any fishermen wear wool socks next to the skin because of the fiber coarseness. Instead, many wear fine-knit cotton socks inside the wool socks or inside of sheepskin liners. The socks should be long and drawn up over the pants leg, even pinned if necessary. A loose-fitting boot, with the foot sliding about within, can cause the sock to pull down and end up as a ball in the toe of the boot. Foot perspiration and lack of circulation will make the boot wet inside, particularly if long hours are spent in the ice, putting away fish. The cold of the ice causes an increase of condensation within the boot.

Some boots are insulated, some have built-up insteps. They are all expensive, but you don't save anything on the cheap ones, either. They, along with other special fishing gear, are tax deductible, though. Save your store bills to document your income-tax returns.

No one objects to a man leaving the deck to take care of himself if he gets a knife cut, a gaff-hook puncture in his leg, or a fishbone in his wrist. The slime and blood and the rust are rich in bacteria, and a few minutes of doctoring can save much pain and lost time later. And if you *do* have an accident, the consequences may have to be shared by all, so do let your skipper know. This is especially important if the cause is from a broken or deficient piece of equipment on deck.

CHAPTER 11

Bits and Pieces

You have by now waded through quite a number of do's and don'ts; still, scraps of information have, no doubt, been left behind; we'll see if we can pick up a few such bits and pieces.

Let's talk about your oilskins; they have, at times, been dubbed "the fisherman's uniform," a pretty well-fitting name, and one of which no seafaring man need feel ashamed.

Most of the work on deck is of such a nature that oilskins must be worn in order for a man to keep reasonably dry. In point of fact, oilskins should be worn in all manner of deck work, wet or dry, because oilskins don't just keep you dry, they also prevent your fishing clothes from becoming too dirty too fast.

Besides, your oilskins protect you. A flying longline hook or a "jagger" on an old wire rope can get a real good grip on your fishing shirt or pants. With oilskins on, you would stand a pretty good chance of getting away from such an encounter scot free.

Don't wear too much clothing under your oilskins. A suit of oilskins conserves body heat very well. You should feel chilly when you first come on deck. It is time-consuming to remove extra clothing when you begin to warm up from exercise.

If you go out in a dory or a skiff, whether for business, recreation, or salvation, wear your oilskins; you will be snug and warm when the fellow without oilskins is kept busy trying to control his chattering teeth.

In case you should be forced to abandon ship, be sure to have your oilskins along when you make the final jump from the deck into the lifeboat or life raft. Here is a case where your oilskin suit may well make the difference between your survival or your extinction.

The drying-out of wet, heavy fishing clothes can be quite a problem on a fishing boat, especially on a smaller and/or older one. No cook worth his salt will tolerate drying clothes around his galley range. This is not meanness, it's common sense and entirely proper, because the range and its vicinity is where the food is prepared. But exceptions to this may be made at night when food is not being prepared.

Sometimes the engine room is roomy enough so that the engineer will let the crewmen use certain parts of it as a drying room. Many engine rooms, however, are forbidden territory, for good and valid reasons. If you do get permission to hang your wet clothes in the engine room, you must, of course, hang your things in the spot which the engineer (or skipper) has pointed out to you, and *nowhere else!* A garment of whatever kind, hung in the wrong place, may be sucked into an air intake or caught by a belt or a turning shaft, and cause all manner of damage to the engine or to other machinery, to say nothing of what becomes of your clothes.

There usually will be some provision for drying your clothing, which, at the end of the watch on deck, will be damp from perspiration and from condensation inside your oilskins. And those oilskins, along with gloves and wristlets, should be washed before being hung up to dry.

What if you should be real unlucky and get a big tear in your fishing shirt or fishing pants? You can't just toss a garment away and get a new one, because the nearest outfitting store may be some hundreds of miles away. So what do you do? You *mend* it, that's what. You have your sewing kit and plenty of woolen yarn; a herringbone stitch and woolen yarn will make a very respectable repair job. With a little practice you'll be able to make it a very neat job, too.

If you should rip or tear your oilskins, use your first spare moment to sew the rip together. The sewing kit does just as well for oilskins as for your cloth garments, but you may have to use two or three strands of yarn for the job. For more elaborate patching or mending of oilskins, there are plastic menders on the market.

Do you know how to use a pair of oars? To row a boat, that is. If not, go rent yourself a fourteen- or sixteen-foot skiff, or, still better, borrow an old dory, and practice rowing until you learn how to handle a pair of oars effectively.

A fisherman/seaman who is unable to propel a rowboat by means of the oars, if and when the conditions demand, is a pitiful sight to behold, and a most foolish-looking one to boot. Learn to use a pair of oars; that ability might save your life if you should suffer a shipwreck.

It may not be probable, but it is possible, that at some time in your fishing career you may have to use a small boat to survive, or an inflatable life raft, or a life preserver, or a fire extinguisher.

Take a good hard speculative look at these items, ask some questions, and don't take no for an answer. It's your life that you're concerned about.

Attend a life-raft inflation demonstration. Try on a life preserver, and be able to find it in the dark. Know where the fire extinguishers are and how to use them. When these items are needed, they are needed fast. You may be the one that has to make the decision. It is too late then to learn how they are used.

In some fisheries, especially in the year-round fisheries such as otter-trawling, a certain number of harbor days are unavoidable due to weather conditions.

Do you enjoy reading? If so, be sure to bring plenty of reading material with you when you go to sea. Long harbor days will seem ever so much longer if you run out of reading matter. Remember, the friendly public library is a long way off, and there will be no newsstand close at hand, either!

If you are a fisherman who uses reading glasses only, you are more fortunate than the man who must use glasses on deck. Fog, rain, and spray make it difficult to see clearly, and many anti-fog treatments on lenses have been tried with varying success. If eyeglasses are necessary, a lanyard from one bow to the other, passing around the back of the neck or head, is a valuable assist to prevent their loss if knocked off.

There are other fishermen with eye problems that can be remedied by contact lenses. This is an ideal answer if you can use them, but it adds to the personal chores, since contact lenses must generally be removed before going to the bunk.

There are other personal handicaps that can be overcome. One such happened to be the case of a one-legged man with an articulated artificial limb, and he had been on the boat for a week without the skipper knowing of the handicap. One day the leather harness got wet, and during the off watch it was hung up to dry. The harness dried fine, but it shrank so that the leg could not be "reinstalled" when the man got up in the morning.

The truth was out; the skipper was speechless, for once.

You may well have to seek shelter in an anchorage that may be far from safe as a harbor, but is the only one within reach. It may be exposed to the wind, or to a measure of ocean swells, or to both; or the bottom may be too hard or too soft to provide reasonably good fastening for the anchor. In such harbors you have to stand *anchor watch* during the night.

When an anchor watch is necessary, each man takes his turn in the same order as he takes his trick at the wheel. Your job on anchor is, of course, to watch out for drift of your vessel, and to call the skipper the moment you notice that she is dragging her anchor.

If there is a radar set on board, the job is easy enough, as you can read any change in position right off the radar screen. Without a radar set, much more wide-awake watchfulness is required. In that case, pick yourself a couple of points of reference, and they must be somewhere abeam. A couple of mountain peaks, or a peak and a hill, a couple of tall trees, one tree and one mountain peak, or whatever is available. If one lines up on the other, you have a range, and if one moves in relation to the other, you are drifting.

When you are back on the beam again, sight a landmark across the compass and note the direction of bearing. (The boat may swing about, but the compass bearing should remain the same. If it doesn't you are drifting.)

Remember: A *range* is two landmarks in line (*and* a compass bearing if the nearest one is quite close.) A *bearing*: a compass reading on a very close landmark.

These "tell-tales" let you know when the boat drifts, so check them constantly. On a rocky bottom, you have another tell-tale, because a sliding anchor telegraphs a rumble up the cable when it moves. And don't forget, check the wire on the winch and make certain that the "drift" is not caused by a loose brake, and the wire paying out.

Call the skipper over any uncertainty, the quicker the better.

CHAPTER 12

How Do You Get Paid?

As a commercial fisherman you'll not be on a payroll, remember; you'll get no salary or wages; your only income will be your share of the catch.

There are at this time several methods of figuring shares; we shall have a look at three of them, but there are many others.

1) In the longline fisheries, the vessel takes a certain percentage of the total earnings (called *gross stock*) as its share. What is left is called *net stock*; from net stock are paid the bills for groceries, fuel, ice, bait, and worn-out fishing gear. What now is left is divided equally among the entire crew, the skipper sharing equally with the rest of the men.

2) In some cases, such as the purse-seine and the otter-trawl fisheries, the vessel collects a certain percentage of the stock after specific gear expenses are paid, so that the crew does not pay into the maintenance of the trawl or the seine used.

When the vessel's share has been deducted, the other bills such as groceries, ice, and fuel are paid, and the remainder divided equally among the crew, the skipper being a crew member for this purpose, although most non-owner skippers collect a percentage of the boat's share as a commission.

3) A few vessel owners, mostly in the king-crab fishing fleet, and some few in the two-man trolling-boat fleet, prefer to give the crew a certain percentage of gross earnings, and

keep the rest of the vessel's share. The vessel, or its owner, then maintains all fishing gear and is responsible for all bills, including bills for food consumed during the trip or season. Whatever virtues or drawbacks this method of sharing may have, it certainly does eliminate arguments about which bills belong to crew expenses and which bills belong elsewhere in the settlement. There are inequities in many share systems, but tradition makes change difficult.

If you enter a fishery where the fishermen are organized, join the union. Not only should you join the union, you should become an active, working member; that's how you can help keep your union strong, useful, and democratic.

When the crew belongs to a fishermen's union, there will be a delegate on the vessel, elected by the crew to his job for the current fishing season.

The delegate is your official spokesman, your go-between. Representing the crew, the delegate checks all bills, then makes them available for the crew's scrutiny. The delegate also assists the skipper in the weighing of the catch for the trip or for the season, as the case may be, and sits in with the skipper when the vessel's accountant works out the settlement and divides the money into shares. Such settlement may be for each trip, as in the longline and trawl fisheries, or it may be on a seasonal basis, as in the salmon and king-crab fisheries.

Since the share system means generally that both crew and vessel share some expenses or all, you should understand the settlement sheet. The settlement is yours also. Some tips:

1. Know just which items are boat or crew expenses, and which are mutually shared.

2. Pay particular attention to your share. Note if all your bills are deducted correctly and if the settlement sheet agrees with the numbers on your check stubs. And do it now. Once the share is apportioned and the money banked, it is very difficult to make changes. Generally, corrections must wait until the settlement on the following trip.

3. No one is going to tell you how to spend that hard-

PURSE SEINER

earned cash, but it is well to keep in mind that with long trips and short seasons, that share may give you a false sense of prosperity. In the armed services, there was an old saw that the pay was "twenty-one dollars a day—once a month."

Does the delegate participate in the settling up because it is assumed that the skipper or owner will try to cheat the crew?

Not at all; rather, the delegate is there because two heads are better than one; he is there simply to help prevent mistakes from being made. One of the writers has served as delegate on a number of vessels and participated in a good many settlements. Not once — repeat, not once — during the several years of such service did he meet up with an attempt from the skipper-owner's side to cheat the crew. He has, however, been a party to discovering a number of would-be mistakes — some of which went in favor of the crew, mind you!

The moral? Join your union, elect your delegate, and see to it that he keeps his nose pretty close to the grindstone.

CHAPTER 13

Shore Leave

YOU ARE a fisherman and a seaman; and you want your shore leave. To take a trip ashore is your right, of course, whenever wind and weather and fishing and running between fishing grounds so permit.

You may want to have a "snort" or two during your shore leave, and that also may be a needed easement. One man enjoys having a drink, another man enjoys *not* having one; both of them have a perfect right to enjoy whatever they prefer, up to a point. And the point is right here: your enjoyment must not interfere with the rights of the next fellow.

Before you step ashore, ask the skipper about leaving time. It is the skipper's duty, really, to announce the exact hour at which he intends to leave port, but if the skipper does not do so, ask him. And make certain that you have the hour well fixed in your mind!

Once you know the hour of departure, you have no excuse whatsoever for being late. Make sure that you arrive on board the vessel five or ten minutes before the announced leaving time. Remember, if you don't show up on board on time, the vessel and its crew will be forced to wait for you, and you have no right at all to make other people wait. Especially when such waiting is costing the time of both vessel and crew, which means fishing time, which again means loss of earnings. The adage "Time is money" is more true in commercial fishing than in nearly any other kind of work, because the fish (like the tide) wait for no man. Ergo, be back on board in good time for leaving port!

If you have "hoisted a few" while ashore, be extra careful when approaching your boat. The dock may be slippery, the tide may be out, and the deck of your boat a long way down. Keep a good, solid grip on the stepladder as you slowly descend from dock to deck.

If several boats are tied up abreast, and your boat happens to be on the outside, be careful when crossing the in-between boats: a hatch or a manhole may be open. Remember, if you suffer an injury while on a "lee tack," you may well lose your privilege of free medical attention. The law says: "Disability benefits arising from injury or disease contracted on shore leave is included, *unless due to the seaman's willfull misconduct or deliberate indiscretion.*"* And "getting stewed" is a "deliberate indiscretion," surely. So — be careful!

If you happen to have the first wheel turn when leaving port, you must, of course, be dead sober when returning from shore leave. An inebriated man at the wheel of a vessel can cause untold amounts of damage and of human misery. No seaman, needless to say, can assume the responsibility for the safety of vessel and crew when less than sober.

Around The Docks

After a trip is unloaded and the boat is washed down and tied to a float or a dock, the boys will be cleaning themselves up while the skipper and delegate are at the store settling up, getting the checks ready. When these two stalwarts get back with the checks and some cash for those that want to go out on the town, the boat will empty of life except for one or two who want to write a letter or perhaps take a nap before that evening out. If several days are to be spent at the docks before going out again, and especially if you are not in your home port, there will be many trips up on the dock.

*Simpson, *op. cit.*

There will also be many trips to the galley or fo'c'sle of another boat to visit friends and swap stories and "get the latest." This is a favorite pastime and most enjoyable, meeting old shipmates and making new friends, trading information and gossip; and it goes on whether you are taking your ease at the galley table, overhauling gear on the deck, or are up on the dock. You are part of a club.

But even socializing is not an unmixed blessing. You may be tied up two or three boats away from the dock or the float, and the deck arrangement of gear and equipment will differ on each boat. There will be something to stumble against on an unfamiliar deck when you return in the middle of the night. Some boats may have carelessly left a hatch open, and the deck lights might be out or be too dim to see well on deck. Gear and stays may hang down from overhead. The inside boat will have fenders out and therefore will be a foot or two out from the float, whose planks may be rotten or slimy from a combination of rain and mossy growth.

If your ship is lying at a dock, you may have a long climb up the ladder when the tide is out, and the ladder will be slippery with seaweed. Some ladders of wood will have broken or loose rungs. Metal ladders are best but may be severely bent from boats rubbing against them. Note particularly if there is a handhold at the top of the dock stringer, to pull yourself up with. Several rungs down, the ladder may be close to a dock timber, giving you only a toehold.

This is the "jungle" in a fishing town. To be alert is to survive whole. But many fishermen stack the odds further against themselves by carrying within a "tankful" of whiskey back to the boat. Those that stepped without looking, slipped, or jumped — and didn't bounce — are either no longer with us or carry the scars of their blunders.

Most docks are in good shape, but make a careful note of the path you follow when leaving the boat. Be aware of the open hatches and the possibly broken ladder (which you may not see when stepping ashore at high tide but which should be a big question mark in your mind when you return that night and see the mast tops of the boats level with the dock).

The safest way to grasp the ladder is on its sides, not the rungs, although at the top the ladder sides may be fast to the timbers so that you must hold the rungs. As you reach up, be certain your next handhold is secure before letting go with the other hand. Step on the ladder with the rungs under the instep, not under your toes. Use special care on ladder and dock if the weather is wet.

If you do drop off the ladder, the chances of landing between the boat and dock are about fifty-fifty, but you will suffer less damage if falling in the water. Many have not survived this drop because they hit their heads on the boat rail as they went by, or were squeezed between the boat and the piling. If in the water, keep away from the outside of the piling; your bones will find 20 to 100 tons of boat to be a rather irresistable force. If unable to climb out, don't wear yourself out. Hang on and holler like hell. Best precaution: travel in pairs if possible.

From the dock to town and back, it's all yours. Have a good time and good luck.

CHAPTER 14

Take Care of the Catch!

WHY DO FISH SPOIL?

IF YOU were asked, "What's the job of a fisherman?" your answer would probably be: "Why, to catch fish, of course!" and you would be half right, for when you have learned to catch fish you have learned the *first half* of the job of a good fisherman. Let's now briefly discuss the second — and equally important — half: how to take care of the fish you have caught so that it can take its place as first-class food and bring you a good price, which means fair pay for your work and a fair return on your investments if you happen to own the fishing boat and the gear.

The first thing to ask is: Why, and how, do fish spoil? "Spoil," says Noah Webster, means to "decay, or perish; cause to become of little value." This last clause is particularly fitting here, because a spoiled fish is indeed, *of little or no value*.

We should bear in mind that the flesh of fish has certain characteristics which make it very susceptible to spoilage. Fish flesh, in comparison with the flesh of warm-blooded animals, has less structural protein and is more tender, more soft. Therefore it is more easily subject to bacterial invasion.

All fish, including shellfish, feed on other animals as well as on plants. This food, be it animal or plant, must be broken down into a number of constituents that can pass through the digestive tract. The first act of this breaking-down process is the chewing of the food; from there on the digestive juices take over and finish the process. But a fish does not have much chance to chew its food, so the entire job of breaking down must be done by the digestive fluids. Therefore, these fluids must be extra strong.

In these fluids, or juices, are agents called *enzymes*, of which some attack the fat in the food; others, the carbohydrates; and still others, the protein portion of the food. Only when this process is finished can the food pass through the digestive tract and be absorbed by the body tissues to provide energy and supply materials for growth.

When the fish dies, the balances in body maintenance are upset. The enzymes, instead of working on the food supply taken in while the fish was alive, will now go to work on the body itself. The chief effect of this is the softening of the flesh. In some cases, that is, with certain species of fish, this softening happens very rapidly. Herring, for instance, if caught when full of certains kinds of feed, may have disintegrated bellies in a matter of a few hours. You may have seen salmon with a discoloration called "belly burns." Such discoloration is the work of enzymes. Also — and even more important — the breaking-down work done by enzymes upon the body of the fish makes it easy for the bacteria to get a foothold, and to get into the flesh of the fish.

Now, when we know this, we realize that if we want to bring a good product to market, the very first thing we must do is to bleed and dress — or *clean*, as the sportsmen say — this fish as soon as possible after catching it.

The action of the enzymes is the beginning, the first cause of spoilage. The second and by far the most important cause is the *bacteria*. Bacteria are one-celled micro-organisms that live and multiply everywhere — if the temperature isn't too high or too low — in the air, in the water, in the soil, on our hands. The railings, the deck, the checkers, and the dressing table on your fishing boat are the home of billions upon billions of bacteria. If all of them suddenly grew to the size of bedbugs the weight of them would sink the boat.

Bacteria usually multiply by splitting — that is to say, when a bacterium has reached maturity it divides itself in two, and now we have two bacteria. Under favorable conditions, bacteria will multiply very rapidly. Some forms of bacteria grow to full size, and divide, in fifteen minutes to half an hour. We know, further, that in temperatures between sixty and seventy degrees the bacteria in fish will grow to maturity and split in twenty minutes.

When the fish comes out of the water there are no bacteria in the flesh itself; the flesh of the fish is sterile as long as the fish is alive. Being that there are bacteria in the water, there are some, not many, really, on the skin of the fish. The gills contain a goodly number of bacteria, and the digestive tract — we generally call it the *guts* — is overpopulated with bacteria. There can be as many as 16 to 17 million bacteria per cubic inch of guts.

Only a few, as we said, are on the skin when the fish comes out of the water, but as soon as it hits the deck and comes into contact with the highly contaminated wood on board, the entire outside of the fish will also be crawling with bacteria. Now drive a pew or a gaff hook into the fish, and what happens? Two things: first, the pew or gaff hook brings about 10,000 bacteria with it into the flesh of the fish; second, the open sore left when you pull out the pew provides a nice easy highway on which the bacteria can travel from the outside to the inside of the fish. The conclusion is obvious. Never, but *never*, should a pew or gaff hook be stuck into the flesh of a fish. In point of fact, such instruments should not be stuck into *any* part of the fish, especially if the fish is to be iced down.

How can we stop this destructive action of the bacteria? Well, we can boil 'em to death — that's what we do in canning — but then we will not have *fresh* fish. There are bactericides that will kill the bacteria, all right, but the trouble is that such poison would make the fish unfit for human consumption, so that will not do, either. We can freeze the fish at a very low temperature. This will kill many of the bacteria and put the rest into a sound sleep. These sleeping ones will, however, wake up and go back to work as soon as the fish thaws. Even so, sharp (quick) freezing is the best method we have to keep the fish from spoiling. Trouble is that only a very few fishing boats on the whole northern Pacific Coast are equipped with proper refrigeration and with sharp freezers.

Since bacteria don't thrive in a cold climate we try to make our fish cold. Now, what is cold? Cold is merely the absence of heat, just like being broke is simply the absence of money. What we have to do is to try to draw as much heat as possible away from the fish, and to do this we use crushed ice.

ICING FISH

Icing fish is not a cure-all. If we leave the fish on deck too long before we get around to dressing it, if we neglect to bleed it, or if we do a careless and sloppy job of bleeding and dressing, much damage will already have been done. And remember this: *damage once done to fish can never be undone*. Once the fish has been contaminated with bacteria, no amount of ice can change that fact. The bacteria are there and will stay there; the best we can now do is to prevent them from multiplying too fast.

We should be generous with the ice; we should never try to save on it. Just how much ice to use depends, of course, on several things: what kind of fish we are dealing with, how long we intend to keep the fish in the boat, and how well the fish hold is insulated; also, it depends on the time of year — on temperatures of the sea water and the air. A ratio of one to three — one pound of ice to three pounds of fish — may be all right with certain kinds of fish, if the trip does not last more than ten to twelve days. Other kinds of fish, such as shrimp and herring, should be iced at a ratio of one to one — one pound of ice to one pound of fish — at the very minimum. The belly cavity and the gill cavity on dressed fish, such as salmon and halibut, should be well packed with finely crushed ice. Also, such fish should be placed in the pen in such a way that the water from the melting ice can run out and find its way down to the bilges, from which it should be pumped overboard every hour — every two hours at the very least. This is quite important, because that water is saturated with bacteria.

Dressing

As soon as a fish hits the deck it should be bled; severing its jugular vein gives the best bleeding result. Proper bleeding will result in firmer and whiter meat, and give the fish longer "shelf life" if it is to be frozen.

If a fish has not been bled, and has to be pacified before you can dress it, take care not to hit the flesh with your club. Such a blow will cause an ugly black-and-blue spot on the flesh; also, it will soften the flesh, thereby providing a prime feeding ground for bacteria. Don't step on the fish. Don't kick it, throw it around, or treat it roughly in any way. Handle your fresh fish gently. Remember always that fish is food. It won't hurt to remember, either, that it is the fish that must provide your pay.

When dressing fish — any kind of fish — take care not to let your knife rip into the guts; even a small cut in the guts will let a few million bacteria out, and most of these will find their way into the flesh of the fish.

Make your cut down the belly: *from* the throat and *to* the anal opening, and then stop — don't cut any further. Do not leave slivers of blood and/or liver hanging on the neck bones of a dressed fish, and be sure to remove all of the kidney — that's the bloodlike substance found along the spine — in the belly cavity. In the case of halibut, it is important to remove every last bit of the ovaries — the eggs or the milt.

CHAPTER 15

Who Started All This?

ι

THOSE with no knowledge of commercial fishing—which amounts to the overwhelming majority of the general public—are prone to think (and talk) of the commercial fishing industry as a "Mickey Mouse" or "peanut-pickin' " occupation.

They are mistaken.

Now, it is true that the business emanating from the harvesting of ocean-grown food is not big business compared to oil drilling, automobile manufacturing, or international banking. Still, one single large processor of seafoods last year sold ocean-harvested products for close to $100 million. Which should tend to show that the business of commercial fishing really does not belong in the peanut-pickin' catagory.

And processing, obviously, is only one phase of the business of converting sea creatures into food for millions of dinnertables — and into a good many gourmet delights as well. First of all, the fish must be caught, a task performed by commercial fishermen by means of commercial fishing vessels equipped with the proper tools of the trade, that is, fishing gear.

Any capital invested in such vessels and equipment?

Out of Puget Sound alone sails, every year, a fishing fleet of around three thousand vessels of several sizes and shapes. These boats represent investments as varying in magnitude as the sizes and shapes of the vessels themselves, ranging from the small troller/gillnetter worth $15 to $20 thousand to the large, modern king-crab fishing vessel built at a cost of well over $1 million. In between those two — the largest and the smallest — one finds a good many different sizes, shapes, and values: salmon purse seiners, otter trawlers, halibut schooners, deep-water salmon trollers. Few of them can be bought or replaced for less than $100 thousand; many of them represent a replacement value of two to four times that amount. Thus, the commercial fishing vessels alone represent an investment of hundreds of millions of dollars. Add to that the cost of the fishing gear — somewhere around $10 million for the king-crab fleet alone — and it becomes pretty clear that the business of commercial fishing is, from a financial standpoint, far from a Mickey Mouse operation.

DEEP-SEA FISHING

History points out that the art of deep-sea fishing was both understood and practiced on the coasts of Washington and British Columbia long before the palefaces found their way to that area.

Halibut was a highly regarded food fish in the coastal Indian tribes; early explorers — George Vancouver, for instance — noted the Indians' use of halibut in their diet. During the last two decades of the last century in Washington, the Clallam County Indians alone harvested as much as up to six hundred thousand pounds of halibut per year. It seems reasonable to assume that Indians outside Clallam County also engaged in the harvesting of halibut; there is no record of their catches available, however.

The first white fishermen of halibut on the Pacific Coast were men from the shores of New England. In the Pacific Northwest they were named "Boston men" — even though their home ports might be in Maine, Massachusetts, Connecticut, or Rhode Island.

A rough and tough lot, they were; not loved, perhaps, but much respected as hard workers and shrewd traders. Their main business on the shores of the North Pacific was sealing — hunting the fur seal on the high seas; but between sealing,

HALIBUT SCHOONER

seasons they had no objection to picking up an extra buck whenever and wherever they could do so.

The first halibut fishery on the Pacific Coast was for local consumption only. An attempt in 1870 to ship fresh halibut "in pounded ice" from Puget Sound to San Francisco by sailing schooner proved to be somewhat less than successful. Similar attempts during the next two decades fared no better, so the halibut fishermen had to be content with a strictly local market until the railroad was extended to the Pacific Coast in 1888.

While some of the eastern schooners engaged in the early halibut fishery only part of the time, others arrived from the East Coast to participate in the halibut fishery on a full-time basis. The "Report of the Commissioner for Fish and Fisheries" for 1888 informs us that

> In the fall and early winter of 1887, three schooners sailed from Massachusetts for Puget Sound. These were the *Millie Adams* and the *Edward E. Webster* of Gloucester, and the *Oscar and Hattie*, of Swampscott, Mass. The two former were owned by Captain Sol Jacobs, who, after dispatching his vessels, crossed the Continent in time to make necessary business arrangment pending their arrival.

None of the three made its fortune as a fisher of halibut, but one of them, the *Oscar and Hattie*, gained a distinction of sorts because the first load of Pacific halibut to be shipped by railroad came out of her hold.

Around 1890, the "halibut steamer" came into being. Often referred to by the derogatory nickname "smoke boats" by the men of the white sails, the halibut steamer nonetheless gave its owner—and crew—a tremendous advantage: it could fight, and conquer, the strong Puget Sound tidal currents, wind or no wind, and was thus able to bring its load of fresh fish to market while the sailing schooner might be at anchor, becalmed, or waiting for fair tide in to port. Could it be that a wee streak of envy prompted that slightly belittling nickname?

The first shipment of fresh halibut via railroad — that which came out of the hold of the *Oscar and Hattie* —

reached its destination, Chicago, in a far from satisfactory condition; those in charge had somehow forgotten that ice will melt when the termperature goes above thirty-two degrees and had neglected to re-ice the halibut while en route. But the Seattle fish shippers learned quickly; later shipments received proper handling and care, and the Pacific halibut soon found good markets in the far-away east.

Halibut fishing (not to mention buying and selling) grew rapidly into a well-paying business; steamer after steamer joined the halibut fleet. Among the pioneer steamers were the *Velos*, the *Iona*, the *Eliza Edwards*, the *Edith* and the *New England*; later additions were the *Grant*, the *San Juan*, the *Roman*, the *Weiding Brothers*, and many others.

Owned by the fishing (fish-buying) companies, the halibut steamers made money for their owners. Their crews, however, didn't fare too well. That was the day when the fishermen were paid by the piece — the piece being worth "two bits," and large or small made no difference. That might be said to be equality with a capital E: a 10-pound halibut and a 100-pound halibut were exactly and absolutely equal, because each brought its catcher the identical reward — twenty-five cents.

The by-the-piece system of payment caused a good deal of trouble between the steamer crews and the steamer owners. It had to go, and it did go, eventually. The new system called for a price of one cent per pound; not much, but a step toward justice, at that: the fellow who had earned himself a set of blisters on the inside of his hands while pulling up a 100-pounder through 100 fathoms of water now could collect a whole dollar for his trouble, instead of the old two bits. And that was progress, any way one looked at it.

With the advent of the internal-combustion engine came still another powered vessel into the halibut fleet: the halibut schooner. Privately owned, often by a partnership of two, sometimes three, halibut fishermen, the first halibut schooners were old sailing vessels converted into power boats by the installation of heavy-duty gasoline engines. A few years later came the "hot-bulb" oil engine; then, after

World War I was out of the way, came the diesel engine, providing cheaper and more dependable propulsive power for the fishing fleets.

Deep-sea fishing never was an easy life; worse still, the men of the deep-sea fishing fleet during the early 1900's were beginning to feel that they were not getting a fair shake, and that their working and living conditions could bear some improvement—in more ways than one.

Shore-side, a man — a green man in particular — looking for a berth on a fishing steamer all too often found himself at the mercy of a crimp, an unscrupulous seamen's boarding house operator, saloon keeper, or other money lender who could sell his services and keep him in perpetual bondage.

On board ship, the "grub" was often none too good or plentiful; often a man would find the fo'c'sle, his home away from home, an anything but sanitary and healthful dwelling, sometimes densely populated with such undesirable shipmates as bedbugs and roaches; and last but not least, the price he received for his catch — one cent per pound — was too low, he thought.

What to do about such grievances? "Organization! That's the way we'll have to go," said the more wide-awake and progressive fishermen. Several attempts to organize were made, all of which came to naught.

Then, in the year 1912, the men from the dories finally came together and formed their own organization, the Deep Sea Fishermen's Union of the Pacific. Their leader and first secretary-treasurer was one Pete Gill, a true and staunch disciple of "Andy the Incorruptible" — Andrew Furuseth, the able organizer and leader of the Pacific Coast sailors. Among the demands listed in the Preamble to the Constitution and By-Laws was the "right to engagement without interference of crimps or other parties not directly interested."

One of the first actions of the newborn union was to demand a higher price for the members' catch; a whopping 50 percent increase, no less, bringing the price of halibut up to 1½ cents per pound! The steamer owners/fish buyers refused, naturally, to meet such an outrageous demand, so the crews walked ashore, and the strike was on — the first fishermen's strike on the Pacific Coast.

And the steamers tied up alongside their respective docks — all the steamers but one: her owner vowed that *his* vessel was going to fish; strike or no strike, he would find a crew.

He did, too. With the help of several crimps he managed to round up the required number of men. True, there was not one single *fisherman* in that bunch; his "crew," it was said, included a few loggers who happened to be down on their luck, but the majority were denizens of Skid Road. Striking fishermen patrolling the docks made no effort to prevent the strikebreakers from boarding the steamer, or the steamer from leaving the dock; they knew, just about, what was going to happen.

Sure enough; a few weeks later the steamer clapped into the dock with a "load" of fifty—that's right, fifty— pounds of halibut in her hold. Her crew hurried ashore as fast as their feet would carry them, never again to be seen on board a fishing vessel. A local newsman who wrote a short item about the "strikebreaking steamer" wondered out loud, "who was the happiest, the crew to get back on solid ground, or the skipper to get rid of that motley crew. . ."

Soon thereafter the strike came to an end. Poorly equipped financially to carry on a prolonged strike, the fishermen compromised and accepted 1¼ cents per pound, or half of their originally demanded raise.

In the schooner fleet, a new and different pay system had been inaugurated: the *share* system. Briefly, the share system meant that the cost of fitting out the vessel for a trip to the fishing grounds and back was shared by all the men on board, and that any and all income from the trip was also shared — the vessel itself receiving a previously agreed- upon percentage of the income, the remainder to be divided equally among the men, skipper included.

This system made each fisherman an equal partner in the venture. True, there was a risk involved; a mechanical breakdown, a long siege of inclement weather, or simply a shortage of fish on the grounds might result in a "hole trip," meaning that the sales value of the catch was less than the cost of the outfit and that each man on board would get a bill instead of a check for his work. The risk was there, and the fishermen knew it; still, risk or no risk, the fishermen accepted the share system with gusto.

A couple of years after the advent of the Deep Sea Fishermen's Union the boat owners followed suit, and formed their own organization, the Fishing Vessel Owners' Association. Since then, there have been disagreements between the two organizations, off and on; strikes have occurred, and lockouts. Harsh words have been spoken on occasion, when emotions overruled good sense, causing bruised egos and hurt feelings — but enmity, never.

In the meantime, the halibut vessel itself had come through a process of changing. As the old sailing schooners that had been converted into motor-driven vessels wore out, a new type of vessel developed: the Pacific halibut schooner.

A crossbreed, of sorts, between a Gloucester schooner and a Norwegian *kutter,* the halibut schooner was a 100 percent Pacific Coast vessel. Strongly built, pleasing to the eye, and an excellent sea boat, the halibut schooner has been called "the queen of Pacific vessels," and rightfully so. Proof of their quality is the fact that a good many halibut schooners, some of them more than sixty years old, are still engaged in various kinds of fishing, halibut fishing included, and are in fine shape, their great age notwithstanding.

As the schooner fleet grew, the steamer fleet dwindled. One reason for this was that most deep-sea fishermen would rather ship on a schooner; the newly invented share system made the fisherman not a hired hand but a partner in the business of catching fish, and enhanced his chances for a more profitable season. Within a few years the halibut steamers disappeared from the halibut banks. The last one to leave was the *New England,* which made her last halibut trip some time around the middle 1920's. The independently owned schooner had taken over the halibut grounds.

The actual work of fishing — setting and hauling of lines —

was done from dories, each manned by a crew of two men. The lines were mostly hauled by hand, or, on deep water, by means of a hand-cranked gurdy. Dory fishing was hard work, and hazardous; loss of a dory and its crew of two was not a novelty in the halibut fishery.

The mechanically driven "halibut gurdy" had been imported from Norway in 1910, and a few of the smaller vessels took advantage of this mechanical helper. But most halibut fishermen deemed it to be a not very practical gadget, and dory fishing continued until forbidden by law, around 1930. Now the halibut gurdy came into its own; every vessel in the halibut fleet put a gurdy on its deck as it was forced to change over the dory fishing to longlining.

Dory fishing was back-breakingly hard work always, and hazardous more often than not. The men who adapted to such conditions and became dory men also became a rough and rugged breed; they had to, in order to survive. Strong, rough, tough — the dory man was proud of his calling; an unknown poet, probably a dory man with a bent for poetry tells about it.

THE DORYMAN

Oh, some can sit in their swivel chairs,
'Midst the cities' rush and rumor,
And fret o'er the cares of the world affairs,
And the woes of the poor consumer.
But I don't envy such gilded ease;
Just give me the salt-soaked ocean breeze,
The lift and surge of the white-capped seas,
And the deck of a halibut schooner.
   I want no fuss with the pale-faced cuss—
   The clerk or piano tuner—
   Who spend their lives in those stifling hives
   In the struggle for more mazuma.
   But give me the windswept ocean's space
   Where the "flat ones" flop in the dory's waist,
   And the salt scud whips in your upturned face,

As you pull for the side of your schooner.
Yes, give me a packet that's sound and tight,
And a skipper with guts to boom her,
Up under the heel of the Northern Lights,
Where the grey seas strive to doom her.
Through the grinding ice, where the groundlines freeze,
Through the howling gales and the pounding seas,
For it's into such tranquil spots as these,
You must drive with your halibut schooner.
> We earn what we get, you can lay to that.
> Though we sometimes pull a boner;
> For the weather that's brewed off Yakutat,
> It can change like a woman's humor.
> When the "queer thing" flies to the schooner's truck,
> We slash our gear and damn our luck,
> But we've time for naught but to cut and duck
> For safety, aboard the schooner.
And then, when our schooner is safe in port,
And we land in a boisterous humor,
You thank the Gods that your stay is short,
And wish you were leaving sooner.
We're rough and we're "coarse" and we're "loud."
What then?
We're the salt of the earth; we're Dorymen—
And tomorrow night we'll be off again
To the banks, in our halibut schooner.

(Reprinted from *Fish and Ships*, by Ralph W. Andrews and A. K. Larssen, Seattle, Superior Publishing, Inc., 1959.)

As the halibut fleet changed from one of steamers to one of schooners, former dory men became boat owners and skippers. Every owner/skipper in that first generation of schooner skippers had gained his fishing experience as a dory man. They adapted to their new and more complex job in the pilothouse as readily as they once had adapted to the rough and rugged work in the dory, and became highly successful fishing skippers — some of them outstandingly so. When the halibut fishery inside a rather short span of time became the most lucrative fishery in the Pacific Northwest — and the halibut fleet one of the most efficient fishing fleets in all the world — it was, in great measure, due to the abilities and the toughness of the dory man turned schooner skipper.

Being engaged mainly in the business of seal hunting, and only part time in deep-sea fishing, the pioneer halibut vessels relied on the crews of Boston men which they had brought with them from their home ports on the eastern shores of North America. As the fleet grew, and deep-sea fishing became a full-time occupation, more and more men were needed for manning the new additions to the deep-sea fleet. Men of many nationalities were recruited into the fishing fleet — as cosmopolitan a group as could be found anywhere.

Immigrants from northern Europe — Norway, especially — now beat their way to the coast; from farms, from mines, and from logging camps they went to join the growing fishing fleet. Within a few years, the majority of most deep-sea fishing crews in the Pacific Northwest consisted of immigrants from Norway. That trend continued for several years, and by the time the halibut fishery reached its peak in productivity, in the late 1930's, some 95 percent of the crews, and more than 99 percent of halibut-schooner skipper-owners, were "imports" from Norway.

While most immigrants from Norway — there were a few Swedes and Danes, too — preferred to "go deep sea," those from southern Europe choose to stay with the inside fishery, for salmon. Immigrants from Yugoslavia, in particular, proved to be adept in the use of the purse seine, and soon became the acknowledged kingpins in the salmon-seining fishery.

The reason, or reasons, for this division into inside fishermen and deep-sea fishermen is not entirely clear. Unconscious nostalgia may have been one reason; those in the first group, perhaps, sensed in the tranquil waters of Puget Sound and the San Juan Islands a similarity to the sunny shores of the Adriatic Sea and the smiling Dalmatian Islands they left behind. Those of the second group? The shores of Alaska's coast may have looked to them something like the rocky shores of their old homeland, and the Gulf of Alaska could very well have reminded them of the wide, open spaces of the Arctic Ocean and the Norwegian Sea.

Whatever the reason, the division has, by and large, held true to this day.

THE INSIDE FISHERY

When William Hume and Andrew Hapgood, both Maine men turned Californians, built the first salmon cannery on the Pacific Coast, on the shores of the Sacramento River, they probably did not realize that they were laying the foundation for one of the largest and most lucrative businesses involving ocean-grown food in all the world: the canning of fresh salmon.

The year was 1864; three years later the partners established a second salmon cannery in Astoria, Oregon. And R. D. Hume, William's younger brother, built his own cannery on the shores of the Rouge River, in southern Oregon, only a few years later. The race was on.

Where Hume and Hapgood had led the way, other men blessed with the pioneer spirit soon followed. James Tarte established the first salmon cannery in Puget Sound, at Semiahmoo, in 1882; other early canneries in Puget Sound were those of D. R. Lord, at Samish, in 1887; of D. Drysdale, at Semiahmoo, in 1891; and of E. A. Washon, at Point Roberts, in 1891.

Those were the earliest pioneers in the development of the Pacific Northwest salmon fishery. There were many others. Ashton Wayman Thomas, master mariner originally from Brunswick, Maine, later a Puget Sound pilot, established in the early 1890's Puget Sound's first fish-smoking plant, on Guemes Island, and was instrumental in the starting of a salmon cannery in Friday Harbor a few years later. Captain Thomas widened his sphere of activities to Alaskan waters; Thomas Basin, now a part of the harbor of Ketchikan, and Port Ashton, on the northwest shore of Sawmill Bay, were both named for this enterprising sea dog.

Peter Thams Buschmann immigrated from Norway to

Tacoma in 1891; three years later he established a salmon cannery in Boca de Quadra Inlet, in southeast Alaska. A few years later, in 1899, he acquired a cannery site at the northern entrance to Wrangell Narrows, built a cannery there — and started the city of Petersburg!

J. R. Heckman, businessman and salmon-cannery owner of Ketchikan, invented the first workable floating salmon trap in 1907. Misused by large private interests, the salmon trap turned out to be a very mixed blessing; nonetheless, it *was* a clever invention.

Indeed, the fishing industry in the Pacific Northwest was built by the brain and the brawn of many men.

In the early days of salmon canning, the gutting and cleaning — preparing the salmon for the can — was done mainly by Chinese labor. Working for a pittance no white man or woman would accept, the Chinese thus deprived the local laboring people of their livelihood. Which, in turn, resulted in almost constant trouble between the local people and the underpaid Chinese.

Then came E. A. Smith with his fish-gutting machine.

Smith, a Canadian by birth, was a cook by trade, and a man with a good deal of mechanical ability. When friends asked why he spent so much time trying to invent a fish-cleaning machine — of all things! — his answer would be that he intended to "do away with the Chinese through machinery." And that is precisely what he eventually did. His fish-gutting machine took over the work performed by the Chinese laborers. Soon it was dubbed "the Iron Chink" — it is still so named — and E. A. Smith became known (of course!) as "Iron Chink Smith."

E. A. Smith was neither a fisherman nor a fish packer; still his impact upon the fishing industry can neither be ignored nor evaluated in dollars and cents.

Epilogue

THE choice (or necessity) of being a commercial fisherman today is really a decision about a way of making money. There are other trades where more or less income can be generated, and other fringe benefits received.

But there is a presumption that, when equivalent earnings are available elsewhere, a person going commercial fishing by choice is looking for different values.

One of the ideas advanced and generally agreed upon by some economists, sociologists, and fishermen themselves, is this idea that fishermen have more than an ordinary amount of freedom, of independence. This is a generality that varies, of course, from fishery to fishery.

For precision, then, reduce this to the Pacific Northwest fisheries, and to those vessels in which a crew of one or more is employed besides the skipper.

Trawling for bottom fish and shrimp; long-lining for halibut and black cod; pot-fishing for Dungeness, king, and tanner crab; purse-seining for salmon; and, to some extent, trolling for salmon and albacore: these are the fisheries most typical of the area. Others, like scallop-dredging or pot-fishing for fish, are minor fisheries now.

These fisheries generate fair to very good incomes, and the stories of big seasons have a basis in fact. But these are exceptional in most cases, and do not reflect the average.

Since the seasons are quite short in many of these

fisheries, most incomes are quite high considering the real time spent fishing, but this is an advantage over shore wages only if a fisherman has a skill to employ while ashore during the off season, a skill that he can come back to each year. Many do. Some without these other skills resort to unemployment compensation; others drift away from fishing because of the uncertainties or because of a bad year.

Some commercial fishermen follow their trade the year round by moving from summer fishing to a winter fishery, such as long-lining in the summer, trawling in the winter. But this by no means keeps all commercial fishermen busy fishing the year round.

Therefore, an element of the freedom we are talking about can be a change, the cycle of moving from one fishery to another, or the cyclic balance of a comfortable shore job in winter and a summer job at sea. This is a stimulating arrangement, a kind of freedom most wage earners do not have, an extra income fishing seems to pay for giving up the security in building seniority in a permanent job ashore.

The prerogatives of seniority and the fringe benefits in working conditions ashore are not a totally unmitigated good. The fisherman surrenders these fringe benefits in return for not just a better income at sea, but for a freedom *from* something he is leaving behind. What he is leaving is the negative aspects of his life ashore, and the list is considerable, varying according to the values of the man, his conditioning, his tolerance.

Some of these negatives are:

Punching a time clock: the hourly payment for a physical presence, like the rent on a house or a car. This is viewed as a degradation by some.

Nit-picking, over-the-shoulder supervision. The boss is paid to be boss, so his visibility as supervisor is kept high.

Restriction of capabilities: the frustration of working at a pace below one's capacity.

Regimentation. One body among many, last name first. Saturation seating on the bus and the plane. Waiting in line for a theater ticket, unemployment check, or a hamburger.

In return for an escape from the above negatives, and others, the fisherman pays what appears to be a high price in hardship, long hours, and a restricted life at sea. It is not entirely true to say he has greater freedom, because he has to submit to a very tough taskmaster that demands and gets more from him than is ever attempted ashore.

As a consequence, to say a fisherman has greater freedom is not so true as to say he has *other* freedoms.

On balance, he pays for this independence by submitting to a more harsh discipline, and does so willingly because, in large part, it is self-imposed. Not everyone will pay the price, and it is at this point of awareness that men will either turn to another trade or remain as fishermen.

It is not entirely true to say that at sea one of the fisherman's hardships is to be deprived of some shoreside social amenities. On the contrary, because of absense of these obligatory amenities, he is more free to do the job at hand without any conflict, and to the full limit of his capabilities. In the crew, he is with shipmates of like mind and capabilities. The self-imposed harness does not gall like the limits of work imposed in a shore job.

If any policing or criticism of the quality of work is needed, it mostly comes from shipmates rather than the skipper. Minute supervision is not wanted, nor is it generally needed. It bears repeating that on a well-run vessel few words are needed.

Individual merit is recognized and respected. The fisherman objects to being checked up on, and to do over a job just completed by another is offensive. But if there is a necessity for doing that job over, words of explanation are not needed. Actions communicate without words, with less likelihood of giving or taking offense. The signals are understood.

Probably the most singular and most unique feature of fishing is the extremely long hours. A sixteen-hour day is virtually a minimum; eighteen hours a day is common. The reward is what goes in the hold, and the subsequent days off in town. It is interesting to note that recently some industries ashore are beginning to compress the forty-hour week into four days, and are surprised that so many workers like and support the idea. There are possibly other "discoveries" of like nature to be found, if management would take the trouble to look at and live the part imposed on its work force.

A man's capabilities aren't limitless, but when working at or near limits of physical endurance, it is surprising how far these limits can be extended, and the personal satisfaction this generates. But a man is not pushed there and cannot be pushed there. He is pulled by the incentives of more pay, recognition of personal worth, and the satisfactions in the job itself.

A singular aspect of shipmates in a crew is that even years after having been together, there seems to be a personal regard for each other that is not generally accorded to a colleague on a shore job.

Yes, there is freedom in being a fisherman, but it is a trade-off inasmuch as you must also submit to restrictions and limits you do not have now.

The foregoing details of living on a fishing vessel, the faint outline sketched in this epilogue, are not complete because there are nearly as many variations as there are fishermen.

The fishing industry doesn't make men, it wants them.

What is expected of you is a measure of what you *may* get in return. Fishing isn't harsh but it very firmly rejects any fudging. After shipmates have been living together for weeks in the same fo'c'sle, the social varnish erodes. The whole man, whatever he is, is exposed. You.

Good luck, good fishing.

Glossary of Terms

BELAYING PIN: A pin a foot or more in length set in the shrouds, onto which running rigging is hung or belayed in coils.

BOAT SHARE: The percentage of the gross which goes to the vessel owner.

CHANCE (*a* chance): A job or a commitment for a job on a boat. Northwest fishermen look for a *chance*; East Coast fishermen look for a *site*.

CHIEF: The engineer, the man responsible for care of engines and deck machinery.

COMPANIONWAY: Entrance/stairway from deck to fo'c'sle and engine room.

CROSSING: Section in the fishhold from one side to the other.

DELEGATE: Member of the crew elected by his fellows to be their spokesman. Has same function as a shop steward ashore.

DRAWBUCKET: Bucket with a lanyard fastened to its handle, used on deck for taking up fresh seawater, etc.

EXPENSES: All costs of making the trip: fuel, groceries, ice, bait, lost or condemned gear. Some expenses may be gross-stock expenses, that is, costs levied against the gross stock before any shares are deducted. Crew expenses are those trip costs levied against the crew's share, which is that amount left after deduction of boat share and gross-stock expense.

FO'C'SLE: Forecastle. Crew's quarters on board fishing vessels, in the bow.

FOOTROPE: Bottom line on a trawl. Corresponds to leadline on seine.

GALLEY: Ship's kitchen and/or mess hall.

GEAR: Implements used for catching fish: nets, hooks, seines, lines.

GOING IN THE HOLE: Having to pay the trip's bills out of pocket because income from trip was insufficient for that purpose. A hole bill is incurred.

GONY: Large seabird of the albatross family.

GROSS STOCK: Total amount of money from sale of all fish.

GURDY, GURDIES: Special winch or winches for hauling of longlines and trolling lines.

GURRY: Combination of fish slime, blood, and visceral fluids that spill while dressing fish. Also the "soup" sometimes found in fishhold bilges—a combination of water and fish wastes.

GYPSYHEAD: A metal drum with a smooth concave surface, usually mounted on a winch. Several wraps of line around the gypsy provide enough friction while it is turning to raise heavy loads smoothly because the line slips and is easily controlled like the friction on a clutch plate.

HALYARD: A line running through a block or eye for hoisting sails, flags, etc.

HANGING: 1) To fasten or sew lines onto web or nets. 2) The distance between knots when hanging: a five-inch hanging, for example.

HEAD: The toilet on board ship.

HEADROPE: Top line on a trawl. Corresponds to corkline on a net.

HOME RUN: Journey from fishing grounds to port.

KINK: A short nap.

KNOT: A measure of time multiplied by distance, equalling speed. One knot equals one nautical mile (6080 feet) in one hour.

LANYARD: A short length of rope or line used for fastening things down on deck, and as an extension of a handle, as in a draw-bucket.

MASTHEAD: The point below the top of the mast where shrouds and stays are fastened. Masthead light: a white light at the mast-head visible twenty compass points.

MUG-UP: A snack between meals, a cup of coffee and a sandwich.

PEN BOARDS: Wod or metal removable dividers which separate parts of the hold and fit into vertical slots or cleats. Usually about eight inches by five feet.

R.D.F.: Radio direction finder.

RUNNING RIGGING: Lines that move through blocks for lifting booms, which are hauled on for lifting purposes.

SETTLING UP: The process of totaling the bills and computing the shares. The settlement is the term for the accounting sheet for a trip, and is sometimes used synonomously for the share. Economists and East Coast fisheries call it the *lay*.

SHARE; SHARE SYSTEM: Formula for dividing earnings between vessel and crew. On the East Coast, sometimes called the *lay*.

SHELF: A heavy, wide horizontal timber used to stiffen the sides of a vessel and located near the top of the ribs, just under the deck beams. The doors or ventilating openings are usually between the shelf and the deck planking, and when open permit air to circulate between the inside and outside skin. This speeds the drying of the wood and prevents the onset of dry rot.

SHROUDS: Wire ropes on each side of the hull, extending from rail to mast top.

SIDEPENS: Compartments each side of the hold, sometimes called wingpens.

SKIN: The outside and inside planking of the hull.

SLAUGHTERHOUSES: The square compartments in the hold along the vessel's center line.

SLOP BUCKET: A bucket or can for galley wastes.

SOU'WESTER: A wide-brimmed watertight oilskin hat for rain or foul weather.

SPRING LINES: Tie-up lines, or mooring lines, used in addition to bow and stern lines at the dock. The spring lines from boat to dock run nearly parallel to the vessel, and are used to keep her from sagging forward or aft in a wind or tide.

STANDING RIGGING: Cables and lines used as fixed stays or shrouds that hold masts in position. Their tension is adjusted by *turnbuckles.*

STAY: Wire rope running from masthead to bow of vessel.

TAPER: To cut web according to a given formula for fitting into a trawl.

TRAWL: A cone-shaped net, towed through midwater or along the sea bottom to catch fish. A trawl may be held open by a long beam (beam trawl) or by otter boards (otter trawl).

TROLLING: Fishing with deep-trailing lines behind a moving boat.

UNDER WAY: Vessel in forward motion; running.

WRISTLET; WRISTER: A cloth tube worn on the arm, extending from the elbow and covering the wrists, with a thumb loop to hold it in place. Keeps arms warm. Fish blood and slime are more easily washed out from these than from shirt sleeves. Most fishermen cut off workshirt sleeves, generally about halfway between elbow and wrist.